MW01007988

SOPHENE

Published by Sophene 2019

Japanese Tales was first published in 2019 by Sophene Pty Ltd.

These tales were compiled and translated to the English language by
Yei Theodora Ozaki and Grace James.

www.sophenebooks.com

ISBN-13: 978-1-925937-15-2

JAPANESE TALES

A COLLECTION OF CLASSIC JAPANESE FOLK TALES

JAPANESE TALES

A COLLECTION OF CLASSIC JAPANESE FOLK TALES

CONTENTS

THE TONGUE-CUT SPARROW

Long, long ago in Japan there lived an old man and his wife. The old man was a good, kind-hearted, hard-working old fellow, but his wife was a regular cross-patch, who spoiled the happiness of her home by her scolding tongue. She was always grumbling about something from morning to night. The old man had for a long time ceased to take any notice of her crossness. He was out most of the day at work in the fields, and as he had no child, for his amusement when he came home, he kept a tame sparrow. He loved the little bird just as much as if she had been his child.

When he came back at night after his hard day's work in the open air it was his only pleasure to pet the sparrow, to talk to her and to teach her little tricks, which she learned very quickly. The old man would open her cage and let her fly about the room, and they would play together. Then when supper-time came, he always saved some tit-bits from his meal with which to feed his little bird.

Now one day the old man went out to chop wood in the forest, and the old woman stopped at home to wash clothes. The day before, she had made some starch, and now when she came to look for it, it was all gone; the bowl which she had filled full yesterday was quite empty.

While she was wondering who could have used or stolen the starch, down flew the pet sparrow, and bowing her little feathered head—a trick which she had been taught by her master—the pretty bird chirped and said:

"It is I who have taken the starch. I thought it was some food put out for me in that basin, and I ate it all. If I have made a mistake I beg you to forgive me! tweet, tweet, tweet!"

You see from this that the sparrow was a truthful bird, and the old woman ought to have been willing to forgive her at once when she asked her pardon so nicely. But not so.

The old woman had never loved the sparrow, and had often quarreled with her husband for keeping what she called a dirty bird about the house, saying that it only made extra work for her. Now she was only too delighted to have some cause of complaint against the pet. She scolded and even cursed the poor little bird for her bad behavior, and not content with using these harsh, unfeeling words, in a fit of rage she seized the sparrow—who all this time had spread out her wings and bowed her head before the old woman, to show how sorry she was—and fetched the scissors and cut off the poor little bird's tongue.

"I suppose you took my starch with that tongue! Now you may see what it is like to go without it!" And with these dreadful words she drove the bird away, not caring in the least what might happen to it and without the smallest pity for its suffering, so unkind was she!

The old woman, after she had driven the sparrow away, made some more rice-paste, grumbling all the time at the trouble, and after starching all her clothes, spread the things on boards to dry in the sun, instead of ironing them as they do in England.

In the evening the old man came home. As usual, on the way back he looked forward to the time when he should reach his gate and see his pet come flying and chirping to meet him, ruffling out her feathers to show her joy, and at last coming to rest on his shoulder. But to-night the old man was very disappointed, for not even the shadow of his dear sparrow was to be seen.

He quickened his steps, hastily drew off his straw sandals, and stepped on to the veranda. Still no sparrow was to be seen. He now felt sure that his wife, in one of her cross tempers, had shut the sparrow up in its cage. So he called her and said anxiously:

"Where is Suzume San (Miss Sparrow) today?"

The old woman pretended not to know at first, and answered:

"Your sparrow? I am sure I don't know. Now I come to think of it, I haven't seen her all the afternoon. I shouldn't wonder if the ungrateful bird had flown away and left you after all your petting!"

But at last, when the old man gave her no peace, but asked her again and again, insisting that she must know what had happened to his pet, she confessed all. She told him crossly how the sparrow had eaten the rice-paste she had specially made for starching her clothes, and how when the sparrow had confessed to what she had done, in great anger she had taken her scissors and cut out her tongue, and how finally she had driven the bird away and forbidden her to return to the house again.

Then the old woman showed her husband the sparrow's tongue, saying:

"Here is the tongue I cut off! Horrid little bird, why did it eat all my starch?"

"How could you be so cruel? Oh! how could you so cruel?" was all that the old man could answer. He was too kind-hearted to punish his be shrew of a wife, but he was terribly distressed at what had happened to his poor little sparrow.

"What a dreadful misfortune for my poor Suzume San

to lose her tongue!" he said to himself. "She won't be able to chirp any more, and surely the pain of the cutting of it out in that rough way must have made her ill! Is there nothing to be done?"

The old man shed many tears after his cross wife had gone to sleep. While he wiped away the tears with the sleeve of his cotton robe, a bright thought comforted him: he would go and look for the sparrow on the morrow. Having decided this he was able to go to sleep at last.

The next morning he rose early, as soon as ever the day broke, and snatching a hasty breakfast, started out over the hills and through the woods, stopping at every clump of bamboos to cry:

"Where, oh where does my tongue-cut sparrow stay? Where, oh where, does my tongue-cut sparrow stay!"

He never stopped to rest for his noonday meal, and it was far on in the afternoon when he found himself near a large bamboo wood. Bamboo groves are the favorite haunts of sparrows, and there sure enough at the edge of the wood he saw his own dear sparrow waiting to welcome him. He could hardly believe his eyes for joy, and ran forward quickly to greet her. She bowed her little head and went through a number of the tricks her master had taught her, to show her pleasure at seeing her old friend again, and, wonderful to relate, she could talk as of old. The old man told her how sorry he was for all that had happened, and inquired after her tongue, wondering how she could speak so well without it. Then the sparrow opened her beak and showed him that a new tongue had grown in place of the old one, and begged him not to think any more about the past, for she was quite well now. Then the old man knew that his sparrow was a fairy, and no common bird. It would be difficult to exaggerate the old man's rejoicing now. He forgot all his troubles, he forgot even how tired he was, for he had found his lost sparrow, and instead of being ill and without a tongue as he had feared and expected to find her, she was well and happy and with a new tongue, and without a sign of the ill-treatment she had received from his wife. And above all she was a fairy.

The sparrow asked him to follow her, and flying before him she led him to a beautiful house in the heart of the bamboo grove. The old man was utterly astonished when he entered the house to find what a beautiful place it was. It was built of the whitest wood, the soft cream-colored mats which took the place of carpets were the finest he had ever seen, and the cushions that the sparrow brought out for him to sit on were made of the finest silk and crape. Beautiful vases and lacquer boxes adorned the tokonoma of every room.

The sparrow led the old man to the place of honor, and then, taking her place at a humble distance, she thanked him with many polite bows for all the kindness he had shown her for many long years.

Then the Lady Sparrow, as we will now call her, introduced all her family to the old man. This done, her daughters, robed in dainty crape gowns, brought in on beautiful old-fashioned trays a feast of all kinds of delicious foods, till the old man began to think he must be dreaming. In the middle of the dinner some of the sparrow's daughters performed a wonderful dance, called the "suzume-odori" or the "Sparrow's dance," to amuse the guest.

Never had the old man enjoyed himself so much. The hours flew by too quickly in this lovely spot, with all these fairy sparrows to wait upon him and to feast him and to dance before him.

But the night came on and the darkness reminded him that he had a long way to go and must think about taking his leave and return home. He thanked his kind hostess for her splendid entertainment, and begged her for his sake to forget all she had suffered at the hands of his cross old wife. He told the Lady Sparrow that it was a great comfort and happiness to him to find her in such a beautiful home and to know that she wanted for nothing. It was his anxiety to know how she fared and what had really happened to her that had led him to seek her. Now he knew that all was well he could return home with a light heart. If ever she wanted him for anything she had only to send for him and he would come at once.

The Lady Sparrow begged him to stay and rest several days and enjoy the change, but the old man said he must return to his old wife—who would probably be cross at his not coming home at the usual time—and to his work, and therefore, much as he wished to do so, he could not accept her kind invitation. But now that he knew where the Lady Sparrow lived he would come to see her whenever he had the time.

When the Lady Sparrow saw that she could not persuade the old man to stay longer, she gave an order to some of her servants, and they at once brought in two boxes, one large and the other small. These were placed before the old man, and the Lady Sparrow asked him to choose whichever he liked for a present, which she wished to give him.

The old man could not refuse this kind proposal, and he chose the smaller box, saying:

"I am now too old and feeble to carry the big and heavy box. As you are so kind as to say that I may take whichever I like, I will choose the small one, which will be easier for me to carry."

Then the sparrows all helped him put it on his back and went to the gate to see him off, bidding him good-by with many bows and entreating him to come again whenever he had the time. Thus the old man and his pet sparrow separated quite happily, the sparrow showing not the least ill-will for all the unkindness she had suffered at the hands of the old wife. Indeed, she only felt sorrow for the old man who had to put up with it all his life.

When the old man reached home he found his wife even crosser than usual, for it was late on in the night and she had been waiting up for him for a long time.

"Where have you been all this time?" she asked in a big voice. "Why do you come back so late?"

The old man tried to pacify her by showing her the box of presents he had brought back with him, and then he told her of all that had happened to him, and how wonderfully he had been entertained at the sparrow's house.

"Now let us see what is in the box," said the old man, not giving her time to grumble again. "You must help me open it." And they both sat down before the box and opened it.

To their utter astonishment they found the box filled to the brim with gold and silver coins and many other precious things. The mats of their little cottage fairly glittered as they took out the things one by one and put them down and handled them over and over again. The old man was overjoyed at the sight of the riches that were now his. Beyond his brightest expectations was the sparrow's gift, which would enable him to give up work and live in ease and comfort the rest of his days.

He said: "Thanks to my good little sparrow! Thanks to

my good little sparrow!" many times.

But the old woman, after the first moments of surprise and satisfaction at the sight of the gold and silver were over, could not suppress the greed of her wicked nature. She now began to reproach the old man for not having brought home the big box of presents, for in the innocence of his heart he had told her how he had refused the large box of presents which the sparrows had offered him, preferring the smaller one because it was light and easy to carry home.

"You silly old man," said she, "Why did you not bring the large box? Just think what we have lost. We might have had twice as much silver and gold as this. You are certainly an old fool!" she screamed, and then went to bed as angry as she could be.

The old man now wished that he had said nothing about the big box, but it was too late; the greedy old woman, not contented with the good luck which had so unexpectedly befallen them and which she so little deserved, made up her mind, if possible, to get more.

Early the next morning she got up and made the old man describe the way to the sparrow's house. When he saw what was in her mind he tried to keep her from going, but it was useless. She would not listen to one word he said. It is strange that the old woman did not feel ashamed of going to see the sparrow after the cruel way she had treated her in cutting off her tongue in a fit of rage. But her greed to get the big box made her forget everything else. It did not even enter her thoughts that the sparrows might be angry with her—as, indeed, they were—and might punish her for what she had done.

Ever since the Lady Sparrow had returned home in the sad plight in which they had first found her, weeping and bleeding from the mouth, her whole family and relations had done little else but speak of the cruelty of the old woman. "How could she," they asked each other, "inflict such a heavy punishment for such a trifling offense as that of eating some rice-paste by mistake?" They all loved the old man who was so kind and good and patient under all his troubles, but the old woman they hated, and they determined, if ever they had the chance, to punish her as she deserved. They had not long to wait.

After walking for some hours the old woman had at last found the bamboo grove which she had made her husband carefully describe, and now she stood before it crying out:

"Where is the tongue-cut sparrow's house? Where is the tongue-cut sparrow's house?"

At last she saw the eaves of the house peeping out from amongst the bamboo foliage. She hastened to the door and knocked loudly.

When the servants told the Lady Sparrow that her old mistress was at the door asking to see her, she was somewhat surprised at the unexpected visit, after all that had taken place, and she wondered not a little at the boldness of the old woman in venturing to come to the house. The Lady Sparrow, however, was a polite bird, and so she went out to greet the old woman, remembering that she had once been her mistress.

The old woman intended, however, to waste no time in words, she went right to the point, without the least shame, and said:

"You need not trouble to entertain me as you did my old man. I have come myself to get the box which he so stupidly left behind. I shall soon take my leave if you will give me the big box—that is all I want!"

The Lady Sparrow at once consented, and told her servants to bring out the big box. The old woman eagerly seized it and hoisted it on her back, and without even stopping to thank the Lady Sparrow began to hurry homewards.

The box was so heavy that she could not walk fast, much less run, as she would have liked to do, so anxious was she to get home and see what was inside the box, but she had often to sit down and rest herself by the way.

While she was staggering along under the heavy load, her desire to open the box became too great to be resisted. She could wait no longer, for she supposed this big box to be full of gold and silver and precious jewels like the small one her husband had received.

At last this greedy and selfish old woman put down the box by the wayside and opened it carefully, expecting to gloat her eyes on a mine of wealth. What she saw, however, so terrified her that she nearly lost her senses. As soon as she lifted the lid, a number of horrible and frightful looking demons bounced out of the box and surrounded her as if they intended to kill her. Not even in nightmares had she ever seen such horrible creatures as her much-coveted box contained. A demon with one huge eye right in the middle of its forehead came and glared at her, monsters with gaping mouths looked as if they would devour her, a huge snake coiled and hissed about her, and a big frog hopped and croaked towards her.

The old woman had never been so frightened in her life, and ran from the spot as fast as her quaking legs would carry her, glad to escape alive. When she reached home she fell to the floor and told her husband with tears all that had happened to her, and how she had been nearly killed by the demons in the box.

Then she began to blame the sparrow, but the old man stopped her at once, saying:

"Don't blame the sparrow, it is your wickedness which has at last met with its reward. I only hope this may be a lesson to you in the future!"

The old woman said nothing more, and from that day she repented of her cross, unkind ways, and by degrees became a good old woman, so that her husband hardly knew her to be the same person, and they spent their last days together happily, free from want or care, spending carefully the treasure the old man had received from his pet, the tongue-cut sparrow.

THE STAR LOVERS

All you that are true lovers, I beseech you pray the gods for fair weather upon the seventh night of the seventh moon.

For patience' sake and for dear love's sake, pray, and be pitiful that upon that night there may be neither rain, nor hail, nor cloud, nor thunder, nor creeping mist.

Hear the sad tale of the Star Lovers and give them your prayers.

The Weaving Maiden was the daughter of a Deity of Light. Her dwelling was upon the shore of the Milky Way, which is the Bright River of Heaven. All the day long she sat at her loom and plied her shuttle, weaving the gay garments of the gods. Warp and woof, hour by hour the coloured web grew till it lay fold on fold piled at her feet. Still she never ceased her labour, for she was afraid. She had heard a saying:

"Sorrow, age-long sorrow, shall come upon the Weaving Maiden when she leaves her loom."

So she laboured, and the gods had garments to spare. But she herself, poor maiden, was ill-clad; she recked nothing of her attire or of the jewels that her father gave her. She went barefoot, and let her hair hang down unconfined. Ever and anon a long lock fell upon the loom, and back she flung it over her shoulder. She did not play with the children of Heaven, or take her pleasure with celestial youths and maidens. She did not love or weep. She was neither glad nor sorry. She sat weaving, weaving ... and wove her being into the many-coloured web.

Now her father, the Deity of Light, grew angry. He said, "Daughter, you weave too much."

"It is my duty," she said.

"At your age to talk of duty!" said her father. "Out upon you!"

"Wherefore are you displeased with me, my father?" she said, and her fingers plied the shuttle.

"Are you a stock or a stone, or a pale flower by the way-side?"

"Nay," she said, "I am none of these."

"Then leave your loom, my child, and live; take your pleasure, be as others are."

"And wherefore should I be as others are?" she said.

"Never dare to question me. Come, will you leave your loom?"

She said, "Sorrow, age-long sorrow, shall come upon the Weaving Maiden when she leaves her loom."

"A foolish saying," cried her father, "not worthy of cre-dence. What do we know of age-long sorrow? Are we not gods?" With that he took her shuttle from her hand gently, and covered the loom with a cloth. And he caused her to be very richly attired, and they put jewels upon her and garland-ed her head with flowers of Paradise. And her father gave her for spouse the Herd Boy of Heaven, who tended his flocks upon the banks of the Bright River.

Now the Maiden was changed indeed. Her eyes were stars and her lips were ruddy. She went dancing and singing all the day. Long hours she played with the children of Heav-en, and she took her pleasure with the celestial youths and maidens. Lightly she went; her feet were shod with silver. Her lover, the Herd Boy, held her by the hand. She laughed so that the very gods laughed with her, and High Heaven re-echoed with sounds of mirth. She was careless; little did she think of duty or of the garments of the gods. As for her loom, she never went near it from one moon's end to another.

"I have my life to live," she said; "I'll weave it into a web no more."

And the Herd Boy, her lover, clasped her in his arms. Her face was all tears and smiles, and she hid it on his breast. So she lived her life. But her father, the Deity of Light, was angry.

"It is too much," he said. "Is the girl mad? She will become the laughing-stock of Heaven. Besides, who is to weave the new spring garments of the gods?"

Three times he warned his daughter.

Three times she laughed softly and shook her head.

"Your hand opened the door, my father," she said, "but of a surety no hand either of god or of mortal can shut it."

He said, "You shall find it otherwise to your cost." And he banished the Herd Boy for ever and ever to the farther side of the Bright River. The magpies flew together, from far and near, and they spread their wings for a frail bridge across the river, and the Herd Boy went over by the frail bridge. And immediately the magpies flew away to the ends of the earth and the Weaving Maiden could not follow. She was the saddest thing in Heaven. Long, long she stood upon the shore, and held out her arms to the Herd Boy, who tended his oxen desolate and in tears. Long, long she lay and wept upon the sand. Long, long she brooded, looking on the ground.

She arose and went to her loom. She cast aside the cloth that covered it. She took her shuttle in her hand.

"Age-long sorrow," she said, "age-long sorrow!" Presently she dropped the shuttle. "Ah," she moaned, "the pain of it," and she leaned her head against the loom.

But in a little while she said, "Yet I would not be as once I was. I did not love or weep, I was neither glad nor sorry. Now

I love and I weep—I am glad, and I am sorry."

Her tears fell like rain, but she took up the shuttle and laboured diligently, weaving the garments of the gods. Sometimes the web was grey with grief, sometimes it was rosy with dreams. The gods were fain to go strangely clad. The Maiden's father, the Deity of Light, for once was well pleased.

"That is my good, diligent child," he said. "Now you are quiet and happy."

"The quiet of dark despair," she said. "Happy! I am the saddest thing in Heaven."

"I am sorry," said the Deity of Light; "what shall I do?"

"Give me back my lover."

"Nay, child, that I cannot do. He is banished for ever and ever by the decree of a Deity, that cannot be broken."

"I knew it," she said.

"Yet something I can do. Listen. On the seventh day of the seventh moon, I will summon the magpies together from the ends of the earth, and they shall be a bridge over the Bright River of Heaven, so that the Weaving Maiden shall lightly cross to the waiting Herd Boy on the farther shore."

So it was. On the seventh day of the seventh moon came the magpies from far and near. And they spread their wings for a frail bridge. And the Weaving Maiden went over by the frail bridge. Her eyes were like stars, and her heart like a bird in her bosom. And the Herd Boy was there to meet her upon the farther shore.

And so it is still, oh, true lovers—upon the seventh day of the seventh moon these two keep their tryst. Only if the rain falls with thunder and cloud and hail, and the Bright River of Heaven is swollen and swift, the magpies cannot make a bridge for the Weaving Maiden. Alack, the dreary time!

Therefore, true lovers, pray the gods for fair weather.

THE STORY OF
URASHIMA TARO,
THE FISHER LAD

Long, long ago in the province of Tango there lived on the shore of Japan in the little fishing village of Mizu-no-ye a young fisherman named Urashima Taro. His father had been a fisherman before him, and his skill had more than doubly descended to his son, for Urashima was the most skillful fisher in all that country side, and could catch more Bonito and Tai in a day than his comrades could in a week.

But in the little fishing village, more than for being a clever fisher of the sea was he known for his kind heart. In his whole life he had never hurt anything, either great or small, and when a boy, his companions had always laughed at him, for he would never join with them in teasing animals, but always tried to keep them from this cruel sport.

One soft summer twilight he was going home at the end of a day's fishing when he came upon a group of children. They were all screaming and talking at the tops of their voices, and seemed to be in a state of great excitement about something, and on his going up to them to see what was the matter he saw that they were tormenting a tortoise. First one boy pulled it this way, then another boy pulled it that way, while a third child beat it with a stick, and the fourth hammered its shell with a stone.

Now Urashima felt very sorry for the poor tortoise and made up his mind to rescue it. He spoke to the boys:

"Look here, boys, you are treating that poor tortoise so badly that it will soon die!"

The boys, who were all of an age when children seem to

delight in being cruel to animals, took no notice of Urashima's gentle reproof, but went on teasing it as before. One of the older boys answered:

"Who cares whether it lives or dies? We do not. Here, boys, go on, go on!"

And they began to treat the poor tortoise more cruelly than ever. Urashima waited a moment, turning over in his mind what would be the best way to deal with the boys. He would try to persuade them to give the tortoise up to him, so he smiled at them and said:

"I am sure you are all good, kind boys! Now won't you give me the tortoise? I should like to have it so much!"

"No, we won't give you the tortoise," said one of the boys. "Why should we? We caught it ourselves."

"What you say is true," said Urashima, "but I do not ask you to give it to me for nothing. I will give you some money for it—in other words, the Ojisan (Uncle) will buy it of you. Won't that do for you, my boys?" He held up the money to them, strung on a piece of string through a hole in the center of each coin. "Look, boys, you can buy anything you like with this money. You can do much more with this money than you can with that poor tortoise. See what good boys you are to listen to me."

The boys were not bad boys at all, they were only mischievous, and as Urashima spoke they were won by his kind smile and gentle words and began "to be of his spirit," as they say in Japan. Gradually they all came up to him, the ringleader of the little band holding out the tortoise to him.

"Very well, Ojisan, we will give you the tortoise if you will give us the money!" And Urashima took the tortoise and gave the money to the boys, who, calling to each other, scampered away and were soon out of sight.

Then Urashima stroked the tortoise's back, saying as he did so:

"Oh, you poor thing! Poor thing! There, there! you are safe now! They say that a stork lives for a thousand years, but the tortoise for ten thousand years. You have the longest life of any creature in this world, and you were in great danger of having that precious life cut short by those cruel boys. Luckily I was passing by and saved you, and so life is still yours. Now I am going to take you back to your home, the sea, at once. Do not let yourself be caught again, for there might be no one to save you next time!"

All the time that the kind fisherman was speaking he was walking quickly to the shore and out upon the rocks; then putting the tortoise into the water he watched the animal disappear, and turned homewards himself, for he was tired and the sun had set.

The next morning Urashima went out as usual in his boat. The weather was fine and the sea and sky were both blue and soft in the tender haze of the summer morning. Urashima got into his boat and dreamily pushed out to sea, throwing his line as he did so. He soon passed the other fishing boats and left them behind him till they were lost to sight in the distance, and his boat drifted further and further out upon the blue waters. Somehow, he knew not why, he felt unusually happy that morning; and he could not help wishing that, like the tortoise he set free the day before, he had thousands of years to live instead of his own short span of human life.

He was suddenly startled from his reverie by hearing his own name called:

"Urashima, Urashima!"

Clear as a bell and soft as the summer wind the name floated over the sea.

He stood up and looked in every direction, thinking that one of the other boats had overtaken him, but gaze as he might over the wide expanse of water, near or far there was no sign of a boat, so the voice could not have come from any human being.

Startled, and wondering who or what it was that had called him so clearly, he looked in all directions round about him and saw that without his knowing it a tortoise had come to the side of the boat. Urashima saw with surprise that it was the very tortoise he had rescued the day before.

"Well, Mr. Tortoise," said Urashima, "was it you who called my name just now?"

The tortoise nodded its head several times and said:

"Yes, it was I. Yesterday in your honorable shadow (o kage sama de) my life was saved, and I have come to offer you my thanks and to tell you how grateful I am for your kindness to me."

"Indeed," said Urashima, "that is very polite of you. Come up into the boat. I would offer you a smoke, but as you are a tortoise doubtless you do not smoke," and the fisherman laughed at the joke.

"He-he-he-he!" laughed the tortoise; "sake (rice wine) is my favorite refreshment, but I do not care for tobacco."

"Indeed," said Urashima, "I regret very much that I have no "sake" in my boat to offer you, but come up and dry your back in the sun—tortoises always love to do that."

So the tortoise climbed into the boat, the fisherman helping him, and after an exchange of complimentary speeches the tortoise said:

"Have you ever seen Rin Gin, the Palace of the Dragon King of the Sea, Urashima?"

The fisherman shook his head and replied; "No; year after year the sea has been my home, but though I have often heard of the Dragon King's realm under the sea I have never yet set eyes on that wonderful place. It must be very far away, if it exists at all!"

"Is that really so? You have never seen the Sea King's Palace? Then you have missed seeing one of the most wonderful sights in the whole universe. It is far away at the bottom of the sea, but if I take you there we shall soon reach the place. If you would like to see the Sea King's land I will be your guide."

"I should like to go there, certainly, and you are very kind to think of taking me, but you must remember that I am only a poor mortal and have not the power of swimming like a sea creature such as you are—"

Before the fisherman could say more the tortoise stopped him, saying:

"What? You need not swim yourself. If you will ride on my back I will take you without any trouble on your part."

"But," said Urashima, "how is it possible for me to ride on your small back?"

"It may seem absurd to you, but I assure you that you can do so. Try at once! Just come and get on my back, and see if it is as impossible as you think!"

As the tortoise finished speaking, Urashima looked at its shell, and strange to say he saw that the creature had suddenly grown so big that a man could easily sit on its back.

"This is strange indeed!" said Urashima; "then. Mr. Tortoise, with your kind permission I will get on your back. Dokoisho!"[1] he exclaimed as he jumped on.

The tortoise, with an unmoved face, as if this strange proceeding were quite an ordinary event, said:

"Now we will set out at our leisure," and with these words he leapt into the sea with Urashima on his back. Down through the water the tortoise dived. For a long time these two strange companions rode through the sea. Urashima never grew tired, nor his clothes moist with the water. At last, far away in the distance a magnificent gate appeared, and behind the gate, the long, sloping roofs of a palace on the horizon.

"Ya," exclaimed Urashima. "That looks like the gate of some large palace just appearing! Mr. Tortoise, can you tell what that place is we can now see?"

"That is the great gate of the Rin Gin Palace, the large roof that you see behind the gate is the Sea King's Palace itself."

"Then we have at last come to the realm of the Sea King and to his Palace," said Urashima.

"Yes, indeed," answered the tortoise, "and don't you think we have come very quickly?" And while he was speaking the tortoise reached the side of the gate. "And here we are, and you must please walk from here."

The tortoise now went in front, and speaking to the gatekeeper, said:

"This is Urashima Taro, from the country of Japan. I have had the honor of bringing him as a visitor to this kingdom. Please show him the way."

Then the gatekeeper, who was a fish, at once led the way through the gate before them.

The red bream, the flounder, the sole, the cuttlefish, and

---

1   "All right" (only used by lower classes).

all the chief vassals of the Dragon King of the Sea now came out with courtly bows to welcome the stranger.

"Urashima Sama, Urashima Sama! Welcome to the Sea Palace, the home of the Dragon King of the Sea. Thrice welcome are you, having come from such a distant country. And you, Mr. Tortoise, we are greatly indebted to you for all your trouble in bringing Urashima here." Then, turning again to Urashima, they said, "Please follow us this way," and from here the whole band of fishes became his guides.

Urashima, being only a poor fisher lad, did not know how to behave in a palace; but, strange though it was all to him, he did not feel ashamed or embarrassed, but followed his kind guides quite calmly where they led to the inner palace. When he reached the portals a beautiful Princess with her attendant maidens came out to welcome him. She was more beautiful than any human being, and was robed in flowing garments of red and soft green like the under side of a wave, and golden threads glimmered through the folds of her gown. Her lovely black hair streamed over her shoulders in the fashion of a king's daughter many hundreds of years ago, and when she spoke her voice sounded like music over the water. Urashima was lost in wonder while he looked upon her, and he could not speak. Then he remembered that he ought to bow, but before he could make a low obeisance the Princess took him by the hand and led him to a beautiful hall, and to the seat of honor at the upper end, and bade him be seated.

"Urashima Taro, it gives me the highest pleasure to welcome you to my father's kingdom," said the Princess. "Yesterday you set free a tortoise, and I have sent for you to thank you for saving my life, for I was that tortoise. Now if you like you shall live here forever in the land of eternal youth, where summer never dies and where sorrow never comes, and I will be your bride if you will, and we will live together happily forever afterwards!"

And as Urashima listened to her sweet words and gazed upon her lovely face his heart was filled with a great wonder and joy, and he answered her, wondering if it was not all a dream:

"Thank you a thousand times for your kind speech. There is nothing I could wish for more than to be permitted to stay here with you in this beautiful land, of which I have often heard, but have never seen to this day. Beyond all words, this is the most wonderful place I have ever seen."

While he was speaking a train of fishes appeared, all dressed in ceremonial, trailing garments. One by one, silently and with stately steps, they entered the hall, bearing on coral trays delicacies of fish and seaweed, such as no one can dream of, and this wondrous feast was set before the bride and bridegroom. The bridal was celebrated with dazzling splendor, and in the Sea King's realm there was great rejoicing. As soon as the young pair had pledged themselves in the wedding cup of wine, three times three, music was played, and songs were sung, and fishes with silver scales and golden tails stepped in from the waves and danced. Urashima enjoyed himself with all his heart. Never in his whole life had he sat down to such a marvelous feast.

When the feast was over the Princes asked the bridegroom if he would like to walk through the palace and see all there was to be seen. Then the happy fisherman, following his bride, the Sea King's daughter, was shown all the wonders of that enchanted land where youth and joy go hand in hand and neither time nor age can touch them. The palace was built of coral and adorned with pearls, and the beauties and wonders of the place were so great that the tongue fails to describe them.

But, to Urashima, more wonderful than the palace was the garden that surrounded it. Here was to be seen at one time the scenery of the four different seasons; the beauties of summer and winter, spring and autumn, were displayed to the wondering visitor at once.

First, when he looked to the east, the plum and cherry trees were seen in full bloom, the nightingales sang in the pink avenues, and butterflies flitted from flower to flower.

Looking to the south all the trees were green in the fullness of summer, and the day cicala and the night cricket chirruped loudly.

Looking to the west the autumn maples were ablaze like a sunset sky, and the chrysanthemums were in perfection.

Looking to the north the change made Urashima start, for the ground was silver white with snow, and trees and bamboos were also covered with snow and the pond was thick with ice.

And each day there were new joys and new wonders for Urashima, and so great was his happiness that he forgot everything, even the home he had left behind and his parents and his own country, and three days passed without his even thinking of all he had left behind. Then his mind came back to him and he remembered who he was, and that he did not belong to this wonderful land or the Sea King's palace, and he said to himself:

"O dear! I must not stay on here, for I have an old father and mother at home. What can have happened to them all this time? How anxious they must have been these days when I did not return as usual. I must go back at once without letting one more day pass." And he began to prepare for the journey in great haste.

Then he went to his beautiful wife, the Princess, and bowing low before her he said:

"Indeed, I have been very happy with you for a long time, Otohime Sama" (for that was her name), "and you have been kinder to me than any words can tell. But now I must say good-by. I must go back to my old parents."

Then Otohime Sama began to weep, and said softly and sadly:

"Is it not well with you here, Urashima, that you wish to leave me so soon? Where is the haste? Stay with me yet another day only!"

But Urashima had remembered his old parents, and in Japan the duty to parents is stronger than everything else, stronger even than pleasure or love, and he would not be persuaded, but answered:

"Indeed, I must go. Do not think that I wish to leave you. It is not that. I must go and see my old parents. Let me go for one day and I will come back to you."

"Then," said the Princess sorrowfully, "there is nothing to be done. I will send you back to-day to your father and mother, and instead of trying to keep you with me one more day, I shall give you this as a token of our love—please take it back with you;" and she brought him a beautiful lacquer box tied about with a silken cord and tassels of red silk.

Urashima had received so much from the Princess already that he felt some compunction in taking the gift, and said:

"It does not seem right for me to take yet another gift

from you after all the many favors I have received at your hands, but because it is your wish I will do so," and then he added:

"Tell me what is this box?"

"That," answered the Princess "is the tamate-bako (Box of the Jewel Hand), and it contains something very precious. You must not open this box, whatever happens! If you open it something dreadful will happen to you! Now promise me that you will never open this box!"

And Urashima promised that he would never, never open the box whatever happened.

Then bidding good-by to Otohime Sama he went down to the seashore, the Princess and her attendants following him, and there he found a large tortoise waiting for him.

He quickly mounted the creature's back and was carried away over the shining sea into the East. He looked back to wave his hand to Otohime Sama till at last he could see her no more, and the land of the Sea King and the roofs of the wonderful palace were lost in the far, far distance. Then, with his face turned eagerly towards his own land, he looked for the rising of the blue hills on the horizon before him.

At last the tortoise carried him into the bay he knew so well, and to the shore from whence he had set out. He stepped on to the shore and looked about him while the tortoise rode away back to the Sea King's realm.

But what is the strange fear that seizes Urashima as he stands and looks about him? Why does he gaze so fixedly at the people that pass him by, and why do they in turn stand and look at him? The shore is the same and the hills are the same, but the people that he sees walking past him have very different faces to those he had known so well before.

Wondering what it can mean he walks quickly towards his old home. Even that looks different, but a house stands on the spot, and he calls out:

"Father, I have just returned!" and he was about to enter, when he saw a strange man coming out.

"Perhaps my parents have moved while I have been away, and have gone somewhere else," was the fisherman's thought. Somehow he began to feel strangely anxious, he could not tell why.

"Excuse me," said he to the man who was staring at him, "but till within the last few days I have lived in this house. My name is Urashima Taro. Where have my parents gone whom I left here?"

A very bewildered expression came over the face of the man, and, still gazing intently on Urashima's face, he said:

"What? Are you Urashima Taro?"

"Yes," said the fisherman, "I am Urashima Taro!"

"Ha, ha!" laughed the man, "you must not make such jokes. It is true that once upon a time a man called Urashima Taro did live in this village, but that is a story three hundred years old. He could not possibly be alive now!"

When Urashima heard these strange words he was frightened, and said:

"Please, please, you must not joke with me, I am greatly perplexed. I am really Urashima Taro, and I certainly have not lived three hundred years. Till four or five days ago I lived on this spot. Tell me what I want to know without more joking, please."

But the man's face grew more and more grave, and he answered:

"You may or may not be Urashima Taro, I don't know.

But the Urashima Taro of whom I have heard is a man who lived three hundred years ago. Perhaps you are his spirit come to revisit your old home?"

"Why do you mock me?" said Urashima. "I am no spirit! I am a living man—do you not see my feet;" and "don-don," he stamped on the ground, first with one foot and then with the other to show the man. (Japanese ghosts have no feet.)

"But Urashima Taro lived three hundred years ago, that is all I know; it is written in the village chronicles," persisted the man, who could not believe what the fisherman said.

Urashima was lost in bewilderment and trouble. He stood looking all around him, terribly puzzled, and, indeed, something in the appearance of everything was different to what he remembered before he went away, and the awful feeling came over him that what the man said was perhaps true. He seemed to be in a strange dream. The few days he had spent in the Sea King's palace beyond the sea had not been days at all: they had been hundreds of years, and in that time his parents had died and all the people he had ever known, and the village had written down his story. There was no use in staying here any longer. He must get back to his beautiful wife beyond the sea.

He made his way back to the beach, carrying in his hand the box which the Princess had given him. But which was the way? He could not find it alone! Suddenly he remembered the box, the tamate-bako.

"The Princess told me when she gave me the box never to open it—that it contained a very precious thing. But now that I have no home, now that I have lost everything that was dear to me here, and my heart grows thin with sadness, at such a time, if I open the box, surely I shall find something that will help me, something that will show me the way back to my beautiful Princess over the sea. There is nothing else for me to do now. Yes, yes, I will open the box and look in!"

And so his heart consented to this act of disobedience, and he tried to persuade himself that he was doing the right thing in breaking his promise.

Slowly, very slowly, he untied the red silk cord, slowly and wonderingly he lifted the lid of the precious box. And what did he find? Strange to say only a beautiful little purple cloud rose out of the box in three soft wisps. For an instant it covered his face and wavered over him as if loath to go, and then it floated away like vapor over the sea.

Urashima, who had been till that moment like a strong and handsome youth of twenty-four, suddenly became very, very old. His back doubled up with age, his hair turned snowy white, his face wrinkled and he fell down dead on the beach.

Poor Urashima! because of his disobedience he could never return to the Sea King's realm or the lovely Princess beyond the sea.

Little children, never be disobedient to those who are wiser than you for disobedience was the beginning of all the miseries and sorrows of life.

THE BLACK BOWL

Long ago, in a part of the country not very remote from Kioto, the great gay city, there dwelt an honest couple. In a lonely place was their cottage, upon the outskirts of a deep wood of pine trees. Folks had it that the wood was haunted. They said it was full of deceiving foxes; they said that beneath the mossy ground the elves built their kitchens; they said that long-nosed *Tengu* had tea-parties in the forest thrice a month, and that the fairies' children played at hide-and-seek there every morning before seven. Over and above all this they didn't mind saying that the honest couple were queer in their ways, that the woman was a wise woman, and that the man was a warlock—which was as may be. But sure it was that they did no harm to living soul, that they lived as poor as poor, and that they had one fair daughter. She was as neat and pretty as a princess, and her manners were very fine; but for all that she worked as hard as a boy in the rice-fields, and within doors she was the housewife indeed, for she washed and cooked and drew water. She went barefoot in a grey homespun gown, and tied her back hair with a tough wistaria tendril. Brown she was and thin, but the sweetest beggar-maid that ever made shift with a bed of dry moss and no supper.

By-and-by the good man her father dies, and the wise woman her mother sickens within the year, and soon she lies in a corner of the cottage waiting for her end, with the maid near her crying bitter tears.

"Child," says the mother, "do you know you are as pretty as a princess?"

"Am I that?" says the maid, and goes on with her crying.

"Do you know that your manners are fine?" says the

mother.

"Are they, then?" says the maid, and goes on with her crying.

"My own baby," says the mother, "could you stop your crying a minute and listen to me?"

So the maid stopped crying and put her head close by her mother's on the poor pillow.

"Now listen," says the mother, "and afterwards remember. It is a bad thing for a poor girl to be pretty. If she is pretty and lonely and innocent, none but the gods will help her. They will help you, my poor child, and I have thought of a way besides. Fetch me the great black rice-bowl from the shelf."

The girl fetched it.

"See, now, I put it on your head and all your beauty is hidden away."

"Alack, mother," said the poor child, "it is heavy."

"It will save you from what is heavier to bear," said the mother. "If you love me, promise me that you will not move it till the time comes."

"I promise! I promise! But how shall I know when the time comes?"

"That you shall know.... And now help me outside, for the sweet morning dawns and I've a fancy to see the fairies' children once again, as they run in the forest."

So the child, having the black bowl upon her head, held her mother in her arms in a grassy place near the great trees, and presently they saw the fairies' children threading their way between the dark trunks as they played at hide-and-seek. Their bright garments fluttered, and they laughed lightly as they went. The mother smiled to see them; before seven she died very sweetly as she smiled.

When her little store of rice was done, the maid with the wooden bowl knew well enough that she must starve or go and find more. So first she tended her father's and mother's graves and poured water for the dead, as is meet, and recited many a holy text. Then she bound on her sandals, kilted her grey skirts to show her scarlet petticoat, tied her household gods in a blue printed handkerchief, and set out all alone to seek her fortunes, the brave girl!

For all her slenderness and pretty feet she was a rarely odd sight, and soon she was to know it. The great black bowl covered her head and shadowed her face. As she went through a village two women looked up from washing in the stream, stared and laughed.

"It's a boggart come alive," says one.

"Out upon her," cries the other, "for a shameless wench! Out upon her false modesty to roam the country thus with her head in a black bowl, as who should cry aloud to every passing man, 'Come and see what is hidden!' It is enough to make a wholesome body sick."

On went the poor maid, and sometimes the children pelted her with mud and pebbles for sport. Sometimes she was handled roughly by village louts, who scoffed and caught at her dress as she went; they even laid hands upon the bowl itself and sought to drag it from her head by force. But they only played at that game once, for the bowl stung them as fiercely as if it had been a nettle, and the bullies ran away howling.

The beggar-maiden might seek her fortune, but it was very hard to find. She might ask for work; but see, would she get it? None were wishful to employ a girl with a black bowl on her head.

At last, on a fine day when she was tired out, she sat her

upon a stone and began to cry as if her heart would break. Down rolled her tears from under the black bowl. They rolled down her cheeks and reached her white chin.

A wandering ballad-singer passed that way, with his *biwa* slung across his back. He had a sharp eye and marked the tears upon the maid's white chin. It was all he could see of her face, and, "Oh, girl with the black bowl on your head," quoth he, "why do you sit weeping by the roadside?"

"I weep," she answered, "because the world is hard. I am hungry and tired.... No one will give me work or pay me money."

"Now that's unfortunate," said the ballad-singer, for he had a kind heart; "but I haven't a *rin* of my own, or it would be yours. Indeed I am sorry for you. In the circumstances the best I can do for you is to make you a little song." With that he whips his *biwa* round, thrums on it with his fingers and starts as easy as you please. "To the tears on your white chin," he says, and sings:

"The white cherry blooms by the roadside,
How black is the canopy of cloud!
The wild cherry droops by the roadside,
Beware of the black canopy of cloud.
Hark, hear the rain, hear the rainfall
From the black canopy of cloud.
Alas, the wild cherry, its sweet flowers are marred,
Marred are the sweet flowers, forlorn on the spray!"

"Sir, I do not understand your song," said the girl with the bowl on her head.

"Yet it is plain enough," said the ballad-singer, and went his way. He came to the house of a passing rich farmer. In he went, and they asked him to sing before the master of the house.

"With all the will in the world," says the ballad-singer. "I will sing him a new song that I have just made." So he sang of the wild cherry and the great black cloud.

When he had made an end, "Tell us the interpretation of your song," says the master of the house.

"With all the will in the world," quoth the ballad-singer. "The wild cherry is the face of a maiden whom I saw sitting by the wayside. She wore a great black wooden bowl upon her head, which is the great black cloud in my song, and from under it her tears flowed like rain, for I saw the drops upon her white chin. And she said that she wept for hunger, and because no one would give her work nor pay her money."

"Now I would I might help the poor girl with the bowl on her head," said the master of the house.

"That you may if you wish," quoth the ballad-singer. "She sits but a stone's throw from your gate."

The long and short of it was that the maid was put to labour in the rich farmer's harvest-fields. All the day long she worked in the waving rice, with her grey skirts kilted and her sleeves bound back with cords. All day long she plied the sickle, and the sun shone down upon the black bowl; but she had food to eat and good rest at night, and was well content.

She found favour in her master's eyes, and he kept her in the fields till all the harvest was gathered in. Then he took her into his house, where there was plenty for her to do, for his wife was but sickly. Now the maiden lived well and happily as a bird, and went singing about her labours. And every night she thanked the august gods for her good fortune. Still she wore the black bowl upon her head.

At the New Year time, "Bustle, bustle," says the farmer's

wife; "scrub and cook and sew; put your best foot foremost, my dear, for we must have the house look at its very neatest."

"To be sure, and with all my heart," says the girl, and she put her back into the work; "but, mistress," she says, "if I may be so bold as to ask, are we having a party, or what?"

"Indeed we are, and many of them," says the farmer's wife. "My son that is in Kioto, the great and gay, is coming home for a visit."

Presently home he comes, the handsome young man. Then the neighbours were called in, and great was the merry-making. They feasted and they danced, they jested and they sang, many a bowl of good red rice they ate, and many a cup of good *saké* they drank. All this time the girl, with bowl on her head, plied her work modestly in the kitchen, and well out of the way she was—the farmer's wife saw to that, good soul! All the same, one fine day the company called for more wine, and the wine was done, so the son of the house takes up the *saké* bottle and goes with it himself to the kitchen. What should he see there but the maiden sitting upon a pile of faggots, and fanning the kitchen fire with a split bamboo fan!

"My life, but I must see what is under that black bowl," says the handsome young man to himself. And sure enough he made it his daily care, and peeped as much as he could, which was not very much; but seemingly it was enough for him, for he thought no more of Kioto, the great and gay, but stayed at home to do his courting.

His father laughed and his mother fretted, the neighbours held up their hands, all to no purpose.

"Oh, dear, dear maiden with the wooden bowl, she shall be my bride and no other. I must and will have her," cried the impetuous young man, and very soon he fixed the wedding-day himself.

When the time came, the young maidens of the village went to array the bride. They dressed her in a fair and costly robe of white brocade, and in trailing *hakama* of scarlet silk, and on her shoulders they hung a cloak of blue and purple and gold. They chattered, but as for the bride she said never a word. She was sad because she brought her bridegroom nothing, and because his parents were sore at his choice of a beggar-maid. She said nothing, but the tears glistened on her white chin.

"Now off with the ugly old bowl," cried the maidens; "it is time to dress the bride's hair and to do it with golden combs." So they laid hands to the bowl and would have lifted it away, but they could not move it.

"Try again," they said, and tugged at it with all their might. But it would not stir.

"There's witchcraft in it," they said; "try a third time." They tried a third time, and still the bowl stuck fast, but it gave out fearsome moans and cries.

"Ah! Let be, let be for pity's sake," said the poor bride, "for you make my head ache."

They were forced to lead her as she was to the bridegroom's presence.

"My dear, I am not afraid of the wooden bowl," said the young man.

So they poured the *saké* from the silver flagon, and from the silver cup the two of them drank the mystic "Three Times Three" that made them man and wife.

Then the black bowl burst asunder with a loud noise, and fell to the ground in a thousand pieces. With it fell a shower of silver and gold, and pearls and rubies and emeralds, and every jewel of price. Great was the astonishment of the company as they gazed upon a dowry that for a princess would have been rich and rare.

But the bridegroom looked into the bride's face. "My dear," he said, "there are no jewels that shine like your eyes."

THE FARMER AND
THE BADGER

Long, long ago, there lived an old farmer and his wife who had made their home in the mountains, far from any town. Their only neighbor was a bad and malicious badger. This badger used to come out every night and run across to the farmer's field and spoil the vegetables and the rice which the farmer spent his time in carefully cultivating. The badger at last grew so ruthless in his mischievous work, and did so much harm everywhere on the farm, that the good-natured farmer could not stand it any longer, and determined to put a stop to it. So he lay in wait day after day and night after night, with a big club, hoping to catch the badger, but all in vain. Then he laid traps for the wicked animal.

The farmer's trouble and patience was rewarded, for one fine day on going his rounds he found the badger caught in a hole he had dug for that purpose. The farmer was delighted at having caught his enemy, and carried him home securely bound with rope. When he reached the house the farmer said to his wife:

"I have at last caught the bad badger. You must keep an eye on him while I am out at work and not let him escape, because I want to make him into soup to-night."

Saying this, he hung the badger up to the rafters of his storehouse and went out to his work in the fields. The badger was in great distress, for he did not at all like the idea of being made into soup that night, and he thought and thought for a long time, trying to hit upon some plan by which he might escape. It was hard to think clearly in his uncomfortable position, for he had been hung upside down. Very near him, at the entrance to the storehouse, looking out towards the green fields and the trees and the pleasant sunshine, stood the farmer's old wife pounding barley. She looked tired and old. Her face was seamed with many wrinkles, and was as brown as leather, and every now and then she stopped to wipe the perspiration which rolled down her face.

"Dear lady," said the wily badger, "you must be very weary doing such heavy work in your old age. Won't you let me do that for you? My arms are very strong, and I could relieve you for a little while!"

"Thank you for your kindness," said the old woman, "but I cannot let you do this work for me because I must not untie you, for you might escape if I did, and my husband would be very angry if he came home and found you gone."

Now, the badger is one of the most cunning of animals, and he said again in a very sad, gentle, voice:

"You are very unkind. You might untie me, for I promise not to try to escape. If you are afraid of your husband, I will let you bind me again before his return when I have finished pounding the barley. I am so tired and sore tied up like this. If you would only let me down for a few minutes I would indeed be thankful!"

The old woman had a good and simple nature, and could not think badly of any one. Much less did she think that the badger was only deceiving her in order to get away. She felt sorry, too, for the animal as she turned to look at him. He looked in such a sad plight hanging downwards from the ceiling by his legs, which were all tied together so tightly that the rope and the knots were cutting into the skin. So in the kindness of her heart, and believing the creature's promise that he would not run away, she untied the cord and let him down.

The old woman then gave him the wooden pestle and told him to do the work for a short time while she rested. He took the pestle, but instead of doing the work as he was told, the badger at once sprang upon the old woman and knocked her down with the heavy piece of wood. He then killed her and cut her up and made soup of her, and waited for the return of the old farmer. The old man worked hard in his fields all day, and as he worked he thought with pleasure that no more now would his labor be spoiled by the destructive badger.

Towards sunset he left his work and turned to go home. He was very tired, but the thought of the nice supper of hot badger soup awaiting his return cheered him. The thought that the badger might get free and take revenge on the poor old woman never once came into his mind.

The badger meanwhile assumed the old woman's form, and as soon as he saw the old farmer approaching came out to greet him on the veranda of the little house, saying:

"So you have come back at last. I have made the badger soup and have been waiting for you for a long time."

The old farmer quickly took off his straw sandals and sat down before his tiny dinner-tray. The innocent man never even dreamed that it was not his wife but the badger who was waiting upon him, and asked at once for the soup. Then the badger suddenly transformed himself back to his natural form and cried out:

"You wife-eating old man! Look out for the bones in the kitchen!"

Laughing loudly and derisively he escaped out of the house and ran away to his den in the hills. The old man was left behind alone. He could hardly believe what he had seen and heard. Then when he understood the whole truth he was so scared and horrified that he fainted right away. After a while he came round and burst into tears. He cried loudly and bitterly. He rocked himself to and fro in his hopeless grief. It seemed too terrible to be real that his faithful old wife had been killed and cooked by the badger while he was working quietly in the fields, knowing nothing of what was going on at home, and congratulating himself on having once for all got rid of the wicked animal who had so often spoiled his fields. And oh! the horrible thought; he had very nearly drunk the soup which the creature had made of his poor old woman. "Oh dear, oh dear, oh dear!" he wailed aloud. Now, not far away there lived in the same mountain a kind, good-natured old rabbit. He heard the old man crying and sobbing and at once set out to see what was the matter, and if there was anything he could do to help his neighbor. The old man told him all that had happened. When the rabbit heard the story he was very angry at the wicked and deceitful badger, and told the old man to leave everything to him and he would avenge his wife's death. The farmer was at last comforted, and, wiping away his tears, thanked the rabbit for his goodness in coming to him in his distress.

The rabbit, seeing that the farmer was growing calmer, went back to his home to lay his plans for the punishment of the badger.

The next day the weather was fine, and the rabbit went out to find the badger. He was not to be seen in the woods or on the hillside or in the fields anywhere, so the rabbit went to his den and found the badger hiding there, for the animal had been afraid to show himself ever since he had escaped from the farmer's house, for fear of the old man's wrath.

The rabbit called out:

"Why are you not out on such a beautiful day? Come out with me, and we will go and cut grass on the hills together."

The badger, never doubting but that the rabbit was his friend, willingly consented to go out with him, only too glad to get away from the neighborhood of the farmer and the fear of meeting him. The rabbit led the way miles away from their homes, out on the hills where the grass grew tall and thick and sweet. They both set to work to cut down as much as they could carry home, to store it up for their winter's food. When they had each cut down all they wanted they tied it in bundles and then started homewards, each carrying his bundle of grass on his back. This time the rabbit made the badger go first.

When they had gone a little way the rabbit took out a flint and steel, and, striking it over the badger's back as he stepped along in front, set his bundle of grass on fire. The badger heard the flint striking, and asked:

"What is that noise. 'Crack, crack'?"

"Oh, that is nothing." replied the rabbit; "I only said 'Crack, crack' because this mountain is called Crackling Mountain."

The fire soon spread in the bundle of dry grass on the badger's back. The badger, hearing the crackle of the burning grass, asked, "What is that?"

"Now we have come to the 'Burning Mountain,'" answered the rabbit.

By this time the bundle was nearly burned out and all the hair had been burned off the badger's back. He now knew what had happened by the smell of the smoke of the burning grass. Screaming with pain the badger ran as fast as he could to his hole. The rabbit followed and found him lying on his bed groaning with pain.

"What an unlucky fellow you are!" said the rabbit. "I can't imagine how this happened! I will bring you some medicine which will heal your back quickly!"

The rabbit went away glad and smiling to think that the punishment upon the badger had already begun. He hoped that the badger would die of his burns, for he felt that nothing could be too bad for the animal, who was guilty of murdering a poor helpless old woman who had trusted him. He went home and made an ointment by mixing some sauce and red pepper together.

He carried this to the badger, but before putting it on he told him that it would cause him great pain, but that he must bear it patiently, because it was a very wonderful medicine for burns and scalds and such wounds. The badger thanked him and begged him to apply it at once. But no language can describe the agony of the badger as soon as the red pepper had been pasted all over his sore back. He rolled over and over and howled loudly. The rabbit, looking on, felt that the farmer's wife was beginning to be avenged.

The badger was in bed for about a month; but at last, in spite of the red pepper application, his burns healed and he got well. When the rabbit saw that the badger was getting well, he thought of another plan by which he could compass the creature's death. So he went one day to pay the badger a visit and to congratulate him on his recovery.

During the conversation the rabbit mentioned that he was going fishing, and described how pleasant fishing was when the weather was fine and the sea smooth.

The badger listened with pleasure to the rabbit's account of the way he passed his time now, and forgot all his pains and his month's illness, and thought what fun it would be if he could go fishing too; so he asked the rabbit if he would take him the next time he went out to fish. This was just what the rabbit wanted, so he agreed.

Then he went home and built two boats, one of wood and the other of clay. At last they were both finished, and as the rabbit stood and looked at his work he felt that all his trouble would be well rewarded if his plan succeeded, and he could manage to kill the wicked badger now.

The day came when the rabbit had arranged to take the badger fishing. He kept the wooden boat himself and gave the badger the clay boat. The badger, who knew nothing about boats, was delighted with his new boat and thought how kind it was of the rabbit to give it to him. They both got into their boats and set out. After going some distance from the shore the rabbit proposed that they should try their boats and see which one could go the quickest. The badger fell in with the proposal, and they both set to work to row as fast as they could for some time. In the middle of the race the badger found his boat going to pieces, for the water now began to soften the clay. He cried out in great fear to the rabbit to help him. But the rabbit answered that he was avenging the old woman's murder, and that this had been his intention all along, and that he was happy to think that the badger had at last met his deserts for all his evil crimes, and was to drown with no one to help him. Then he raised his oar and struck at the badger with all his strength till he fell with the sinking clay boat and was seen no more.

Thus at last he kept his promise to the old farmer. The rabbit now turned and rowed shorewards, and having landed and pulled his boat upon the beach, hurried back to tell the old farmer everything, and how the badger, his enemy, had been killed.

The old farmer thanked him with tears in his eyes. He said that till now he could never sleep at night or be at peace in the daytime, thinking of how his wife's death was unavenged, but from this time he would be able to sleep and eat as of old. He begged the rabbit to stay with him and share his home, so from this day the rabbit went to stay with the old farmer and they both lived together as good friends to the end of their days.

THE SHINANSHA, OR THE SOUTH POINTING CARRIAGE

The compass, with its needle always pointing to the North, is quite a common thing, and no one thinks that it is remarkable now, though when it was first invented it must have been a wonder.

Now long ago in China, there was a still more wonderful invention called the shinansha. This was a kind of chariot with the figure of a man on it always pointing to the South. No matter how the chariot was placed the figure always wheeled about and pointed to the South.

This curious instrument was invented by Kotei, one of the three Chinese Emperors of the Mythological age. Kotei was the son of the Emperor Yuhi. Before he was born his mother had a vision which foretold that her son would be a great man.

One summer evening she went out to walk in the meadows to seek the cool breezes which blow at the end of the day and to gaze with pleasure at the star-lit heavens above her. As she looked at the North Star, strange to relate, it shot forth vivid flashes of lightning in every direction. Soon after this her son Kotei came into the world.

Kotei in time grew to manhood and succeeded his father the Emperor Yuhi. His early reign was greatly troubled by the rebel Shiyu. This rebel wanted to make himself King, and many were the battles which he fought to this end. Shiyu was a wicked magician, his head was made of iron, and there was no man that could conquer him.

At last Kotei declared war against the rebel and led his army to battle, and the two armies met on a plain called Takuroku. The Emperor boldly attacked the enemy, but the magician brought down a dense fog upon the battlefield, and while the royal army were wandering about in confusion, trying to find their way, Shiyu retreated with his troops, laughing at having fooled the royal army.

No matter however strong and brave the Emperor's soldiers were, the rebel with his magic could always escape in the end.

Kotei returned to his Palace, and thought and pondered deeply as to how he should conquer the magician, for he was determined not to give up yet. After a long time he invented the shinansha with the figure of a man always pointing South, for there were no compasses in those days. With this instrument to show him the way he need not fear the dense fogs raised up by the magician to confound his men.

Kotei again declared war against Shiyu. He placed the shinansha in front of his army and led the way to the battlefield.

The battle began in earnest. The rebel was being driven backward by the royal troops when he again resorted to magic, and upon his saying some strange words in a loud voice, immediately a dense fog came down upon the battlefield.

But this time no soldier minded the fog, not one was confused. Kotei by pointing to the shinansha could find his way and directed the army without a single mistake. He closely pursued the rebel army and drove them backward till they came to a big river. This river Kotei and his men found was swollen by the floods and impossible to cross.

Shiyu by using his magic art quickly passed over with his army and shut himself up in a fortress on the opposite bank.

When Kotei found his march checked he was wild with disappointment, for he had very nearly overtaken the rebel when the river stopped him.

He could do nothing, for there were no boats in those days, so the Emperor ordered his tent to be pitched in the pleasantest spot that the place afforded.

One day he stepped forth from his tent and after walking about for a short time he came to a pond. Here he sat down on the bank and was lost in thought.

It was autumn. The trees growing along the edge of the water were shedding their leaves, which floated hither and thither on the surface of the pond. By and by, Kotei's attention was attracted to a spider on the brink of the water. The little insect was trying to get on to one of the floating leaves near by. It did so at last, and was soon floating over the water to the other side of the pond.

This little incident made the clever Emperor think that he might try to make something that could carry himself and his men over the river in the same way that the leaf had carried over the spider. He set to work and persevered till he invented the first boat. When he found that it was a success he set all his men to make more, and in time there were enough boats for the whole army.

Kotei now took his army across the river, and attacked Shiyu's headquarters. He gained a complete victory, and so put an end to the war which had troubled his country for so long.

This wise and good Emperor did not rest till he had secured peace and prosperity throughout his whole land. He was beloved by his subjects, who now enjoyed their happiness of peace for many long years under him. He spent a great deal of time in making inventions which would benefit his people, and he succeeded in many besides the boat and the South

Pointing shinansha.

He had reigned about a hundred years when one day, as Kotei was looking upwards, the sky became suddenly red, and something came glittering like gold towards the earth. As it came nearer Kotei saw that it was a great Dragon. The Dragon approached and bowed down its head before the Emperor. The Empress and the courtiers were so frightened that they ran away screaming.

But the Emperor only smiled and called to them to stop, and said:

"Do not be afraid. This is a messenger from Heaven. My time here is finished!" He then mounted the Dragon, which began to ascend towards the sky.

When the Empress and the courtiers saw this they all cried out together:

"Wait a moment! We wish to come too." And they all ran and caught hold of the Dragon's beard and tried to mount him.

But it was impossible for so many people to ride on the Dragon. Several of them hung on to the creature's beard so that when it tried to mount the hair was pulled out and they fell to the ground.

Meanwhile the Empress and a few of the courtiers were safely seated on the Dragon's back. The Dragon flew up so high in the heavens that in a short time the inmates of the Palace, who had been left behind disappointed, could see them no more.

After some time a bow and an arrow dropped to the earth in the courtyard of the Palace. They were recognized as having belonged to the Emperor Kotei. The courtiers took them up carefully and preserved them as sacred relics in the Palace.

THE ADVENTURES OF KINTARO, THE GOLDEN BOY

Long, long ago there lived in Kyoto a brave soldier named Kintoki. Now he fell in love with a beautiful lady and married her. Not long after this, through the malice of some of his friends, he fell into disgrace at Court and was dismissed. This misfortune so preyed upon his mind that he did not long survive his dismissal—he died, leaving behind him his beautiful young wife to face the world alone. Fearing her husband's enemies, she fled to the Ashigara Mountains as soon as her husband was dead, and there in the lonely forests where no one ever came except woodcutters, a little boy was born to her. She called him Kintaro or the Golden Boy. Now the remarkable thing about this child was his great strength, and as he grew older he grew stronger and stronger, so that by the time he was eight years of age he was able to cut down trees as quickly as the woodcutters. Then his mother gave him a large ax, and he used to go out in the forest and help the woodcutters, who called him "Wonder-child," and his mother the "Old Nurse of the Mountains," for they did not know her high rank. Another favorite pastime of Kintaro's was to smash up rocks and stones. You can imagine how strong he was!

Quite unlike other boys, Kintaro, grew up all alone in the mountain wilds, and as he had no companions he made friends with all the animals and learned to understand them and to speak their strange talk. By degrees they all grew quite tame and looked upon Kintaro as their master, and he used them as his servants and messengers. But his special retainers were the bear, the deer, the monkey and the hare.

The bear often brought her cubs for Kintaro to romp

with, and when she came to take them home Kintaro would get on her back and have a ride to her cave. He was very fond of the deer too, and would often put his arms round the creature's neck to show that its long horns did not frighten him. Great was the fun they all had together.

One day, as usual, Kintaro went up into the mountains, followed by the bear, the deer, the monkey, and the hare. After walking for some time up hill and down dale and over rough roads, they suddenly came out upon a wide and grassy plain covered with pretty wild flowers.

Here, indeed, was a nice place where they could all have a good romp together. The deer rubbed his horns against a tree for pleasure, the monkey scratched his back, the hare smoothed his long ears, and the bear gave a grunt of satisfaction.

Kintaro said, "Here is a place for a good game. What do you all say to a wrestling match?"

The bear being the biggest and the oldest, answered for the others:

"That will be great fun," said she. "I am the strongest animal, so I will make the platform for the wrestlers;" and she set to work with a will to dig up the earth and to pat it into shape.

"All right," said Kintaro, "I will look on while you all wrestle with each other. I shall give a prize to the one who wins in each round."

"What fun! we shall all try to get the prize," said the bear.

The deer, the monkey and the hare set to work to help the bear raise the platform on which they were all to wrestle. When this was finished, Kintaro cried out:

"Now begin! the monkey and the hare shall open the sports and the deer shall be umpire. Now, Mr. Deer, you are to be umpire!"

"He, he!" answered the deer. "I will be umpire. Now, Mr. Monkey and Mr. Hare, if you are both ready, please walk out and take your places on the platform."

Then the monkey and the hare both hopped out, quickly and nimbly, to the wrestling platform. The deer, as umpire, stood between the two and called out:

"Red-back! Red-back!" (this to the monkey, who has a red back in Japan). "Are you ready?"

Then he turned to the hare:

"Long-ears! Long-ears! are you ready?"

Both the little wrestlers faced each other while the deer raised a leaf on high as signal. When he dropped the leaf the monkey and the hare rushed upon each other, crying "Yoisho, yoisho!"

While the monkey and the hare wrestled, the deer called out encouragingly or shouted warnings to each of them as the hare or the monkey pushed each other near the edge of the platform and were in danger of falling over.

"Red-back! Red-back! stand your ground!" called out the deer.

"Long-ears! Long-ears! be strong, be strong—don't let the monkey beat you!" grunted the bear.

So the monkey and the hare, encouraged by their friends, tried their very hardest to beat each other. The hare at last gained on the monkey. The monkey seemed to trip up, and the hare giving him a good push sent him flying off the platform with a bound.

The poor monkey sat up rubbing his back, and his face was very long as he screamed angrily. "Oh, oh! how my back hurts—my back hurts me!"

Seeing the monkey in this plight on the ground, the deer holding his leaf on high said:

"This round is finished—the hare has won."

Kintaro then opened his luncheon box and taking out a rice-dumpling, gave it to the hare saying:

"Here is your prize, and you have earned, it well!"

Now the monkey got up looking very cross, and as they say in Japan "his stomach stood up," for he felt that he had not been fairly beaten. So he said to Kintaro and the others who were standing by:

"I have not been fairly beaten. My foot slipped and I tumbled. Please give me another chance and let the hare wrestle with me for another round."

Then Kintaro consenting, the hare and the monkey began to wrestle again. Now, as every one knows, the monkey is a cunning animal by nature, and he made up his mind to get the best of the hare this time if it were possible. To do this, he thought that the best and surest way would be to get hold of the hare's long ear. This he soon managed to do. The hare was quite thrown off his guard by the pain of having his long ear pulled so hard, and the monkey seizing his opportunity at last, caught hold of one of the hare's legs and sent him sprawling in the middle of the dais. The monkey was now the victor and received, a rice-dumpling from Kintaro, which pleased him so much that he quite forgot his sore back.

The deer now came up and asked the hare if he felt ready for another round, and if so whether he would try a round with him, and the hare consenting, they both stood up to wrestle. The bear came forward as umpire.

The deer with long horns and the hare with long ears, it must have been an amusing sight to those who watched this queer match. Suddenly the deer went down on one of his knees, and the bear with the leaf on high declared him beaten. In this way, sometimes the one, sometimes the other, conquering, the little party amused themselves till they were tired.

At last Kintaro got up and said:

"This is enough for to-day. What a nice place we have found for wrestling; let us come again to-morrow. Now, we will all go home. Come along!" So saying, Kintaro led the way while the animals followed.

After walking some little distance they came out on the banks of a river flowing through a valley. Kintaro and his four furry friends stood and looked about for some means of crossing. Bridge there was none. The river rushed "don, don" on its way. All the animals looked serious, wondering how they could cross the stream and get home that evening.

Kintaro, however, said:

"Wait a moment. I will make a good bridge for you all in a few minutes."

The bear, the deer, the monkey and the hare looked at him to see what he would do now.

Kintaro went from one tree to another that grew along the river bank. At last he stopped in front of a very large tree that was growing at the water's edge. He took hold of the trunk and pulled it with all his might, once, twice, thrice! At the third pull, so great was Kintaro's strength that the roots gave way, and "meri, meri" (crash, crash), over fell the tree, forming an excellent bridge across the stream.

"There," said Kintaro, "what do you think of my bridge? It is quite safe, so follow me," and he stepped across first. The four animals followed. Never had they seen any one so strong before, and they all exclaimed:

"How strong he is! how strong he is!"

While all this was going on by the river a woodcutter, who happened to be standing on a rock overlooking the stream, had seen all that passed beneath him. He watched with great surprise Kintaro and his animal companions. He rubbed his eyes to be sure that he was not dreaming when he saw this boy pull over a tree by the roots and throw it across the stream to form a bridge.

The woodcutter, for such he seemed to be by his dress, marveled at all he saw, and said to himself:

"This is no ordinary child. Whose son can he be? I will find out before this day is done."

He hastened after the strange party and crossed the bridge behind them. Kintaro knew nothing of all this, and little guessed that he was being followed. On reaching the other side of the river he and the animals separated, they to their lairs in the woods and he to his mother, who was waiting for him.

As soon as he entered the cottage, which stood like a matchbox in the heart of the pine-woods, he went to greet his mother, saying:

"Okkasan (mother), here I am!"

"O, Kimbo!" said his mother with a bright smile, glad to see her boy home safe after the long day. "How late you are to-day. I feared that something had happened to you. Where have you been all the time?"

"I took my four friends, the bear, the deer, the monkey, and the hare, up into the hills, and there I made them try a wrestling match, to see which was the strongest. We all enjoyed the sport, and are going to the same place to-morrow to have another match."

"Now tell me who is the strongest of all?" asked his mother, pretending not to know.

"Oh, mother," said Kintaro, "don't you know that I am the strongest? There was no need for me to wrestle with any of them."

"But next to you then, who is the strongest?"

"The bear comes next to me in strength," answered Kintaro.

"And after the bear?" asked his mother again.

"Next to the bear it is not easy to say which is the strongest, for the deer, the monkey, and the hare all seem to be as strong as each other," said Kintaro.

Suddenly Kintaro and his mother were startled by a voice from outside.

"Listen to me, little boy! Next time you go, take this old man with you to the wrestling match. He would like to join the sport too!"

It was the old woodcutter who had followed Kintaro from the river. He slipped off his clogs and entered the cottage. Yama-uba and her son were both taken by surprise. They looked at the intruder wonderingly and saw that he was some one they had never seen before.

"Who are you?" they both exclaimed.

Then the woodcutter laughed and said:

"It does not matter who I am yet, but let us see who has the strongest arm—this boy or myself?"

Then Kintaro, who had lived all his life in the forest, answered the old man without any ceremony, saying:

"We will have a try if you wish it, but you must not be angry whoever is beaten."

Then Kintaro and the woodcutter both put out their right arms and grasped each other's hands. For a long time Kintaro and the old man wrestled together in this way, each trying to bend the other's arm, but the old man was very strong, and the strange pair were evenly matched. At last the old man desisted, declaring it a drawn game.

"You are, indeed, a very strong child. There are few men who can boast of the strength of my right arm!" said the woodcutter. "I saw you first on the banks of the river a few hours ago, when you pulled up that large tree to make a bridge across the torrent. Hardly able to believe what I saw I followed you home. Your strength of arm, which I have just tried, proves what I saw this afternoon. When you are full-grown you will surely be the strongest man in all Japan. It is a pity that you are hidden away in these wild mountains."

Then he turned to Kintaro's mother:

"And you, mother, have you no thought of taking your child to the Capital, and of teaching him to carry a sword as befits a samurai (a Japanese knight)?"

"You are very kind to take so much interest in my son." replied the mother; "but he is as you see, wild and uneducated, and I fear it would be very difficult to do as you say. Because of his great strength as an infant I hid him away in this unknown part of the country, for he hurt every one that came near him. I have often wished that I could, one day, see my boy a knight wearing two swords, but as we have no influential friend to introduce us at the Capital, I fear my hope will never come true."

"You need not trouble yourself about that. To tell you the truth I am no woodcutter! I am one of the great generals of Japan. My name is Sadamitsu, and I am a vassal of the powerful Lord Minamoto-no-Raiko. He ordered me to go round the country and look for boys who give promise of remarkable strength, so that they may be trained as soldiers for his army. I thought that I could best do this by assuming the disguise of a woodcutter. By good fortune, I have thus unexpectedly come across your son. Now if you really wish him to be a SAMURAI (a knight), I will take him and present him to the Lord Raiko as a candidate for his service. What do you say to this?"

As the kind general gradually unfolded his plan the mother's heart was filled with a great joy. She saw that here was a wonderful chance of the one wish of her life being fulfilled—that of seeing Kintaro a SAMURAI before she died.

Bowing her head to the ground, she replied:

"I will then intrust my son to you if you really mean what you say."

Kintaro had all this time been sitting by his mother's side listening to what they said. When his mother finished speaking, he exclaimed:

"Oh, joy! joy! I am to go with the general and one day I shall be a SAMURAI!"

Thus Kintaro's fate was settled, and the general decided to start for the Capital at once, taking Kintaro with him. It need hardly be said that Yama-uba was sad at parting with her boy, for he was all that was left to her. But she hid her grief with a strong face, as they say in Japan. She knew that it was for her boy's good that he should leave her now, and she must not discourage him just as he was setting out. Kintaro promised never to forget her, and said that as soon as he was a knight wearing two swords he would build her a home and take care of her in her old age.

All the animals, those he had tamed to serve him, the bear, the deer, the monkey, and the hare, as soon as they found out that he was going away, came to ask if they might attend him as usual. When they learned that he was going away for good they followed him to the foot of the mountain to see him off.

"Kimbo," said his mother, "mind and be a good boy."

"Mr. Kintaro," said the faithful animals, "we wish you good health on your travels."

Then they all climbed a tree to see the last of him, and from that height they watched him and his shadow gradually grow smaller and smaller, till he was lost to sight.

The general Sadamitsu went on his way rejoicing at having so unexpectedly found such a prodigy as Kintaro.

Having arrived at their destination the general took Kintaro at once to his Lord, Minamoto-no-Raiko, and told him all about Kintaro and how he had found the child. Lord Raiko was delighted with the story, and having commanded Kintaro to be brought to him, made him one of his vassals at once.

Lord Raiko's army was famous for its band called "The Four Braves." These warriors were chosen by himself from amongst the bravest and strongest of his soldiers, and the small and well-picked band was distinguished throughout the whole of Japan for the dauntless courage of its men.

When Kintaro grew up to be a man his master made him the Chief of the Four Braves. He was by far the strongest of them all. Soon after this event, news was brought to the city that a cannibal monster had taken up his abode not far away and that people were stricken with fear. Lord Raiko ordered Kintaro to the rescue. He immediately started off, delighted at the prospect of trying his sword.

Surprising the monster in its den, he made short work of cutting off its great head, which he carried back in triumph to his master.

Kintaro now rose to be the greatest hero of his country, and great was the power and honor and wealth that came to him. He now kept his promise and built a comfortable home for his old mother, who lived happily with him in the Capital to the end of her days.

Is not this the story of a great hero?

THE STORY OF
PRINCESS HASE

Many, many years ago there lived in Nara, the ancient Capital of Japan, a wise State minister, by name Prince Toyonari Fujiwara. His wife was a noble, good, and beautiful woman called Princess Murasaki (Violet). They had been married by their respective families according to Japanese custom when very young, and had lived together happily ever since. They had, however, one cause for great sorrow, for as the years went by no child was born to them. This made them very unhappy, for they both longed to see a child of their own who would grow up to gladden their old age, carry on the family name, and keep up the ancestral rites when they were dead. The Prince and his lovely wife, after long consultation and much thought, determined to make a pilgrimage to the temple of Hase-no-Kwannon (Goddess of Mercy at Hase), for they believed, according to the beautiful tradition of their religion, that the Mother of Mercy, Kwannon, comes to answer the prayers of mortals in the form that they need the most. Surely after all these years of prayer she would come to them in the form of a beloved child in answer to their special pilgrimage, for that was the greatest need of their two lives. Everything else they had that this life could give them, but it was all as nothing because the cry of their hearts was unsatisfied.

So the Prince Toyonari and his wife went to the temple of Kwannon at Hase and stayed there for a long time, both daily offering incense and praying to Kwannon, the Heavenly Mother, to grant them the desire of their whole lives. And their prayer was answered.

A daughter was born at last to the Princess Murasaki,

and great was the joy of her heart. On presenting the child to her husband, they both decided to call her Hase-Hime, or the Princess of Hase, because she was the gift of the Kwannon at that place. They both reared her with great care and tenderness, and the child grew in strength and beauty.

When the little girl was five years old her mother fell dangerously ill and all the doctors and their medicines could not save her. A little before she breathed her last she called her daughter to her, and gently stroking her head, said:

"Hase-Hime, do you know that your mother cannot live any longer? Though I die, you must grow up a good girl. Do your best not to give trouble to your nurse or any other of your family. Perhaps your father will marry again and some one will fill my place as your mother. If so do not grieve for me, but look upon your father's second wife as your true mother, and be obedient and filial to both her and your father. Remember when you are grown up to be submissive to those who are your superiors, and to be kind to all those who are under you. Don't forget this. I die with the hope that you will grow up a model woman."

Hase-Hime listened in an attitude of respect while her mother spoke, and promised to do all that she was told. There is a proverb which says "As the soul is at three so it is at one hundred," and so Hase-Hime grew up as her mother had wished, a good and obedient little Princess, though she was now too young to understand how great was the loss of her mother.

Not long after the death of his first wife, Prince Toyonari married again, a lady of noble birth named Princess Terute. Very different in character, alas! to the good and wise Princess Murasaki, this woman had a cruel, bad heart. She did not love her step-daughter at all, and was often very unkind to the little motherless girl, saying to herself:

"This is not my child! this is not my child!"

But Hase-Hime bore every unkindness with patience, and even waited upon her step-mother kindly and obeyed her in every way and never gave any trouble, just as she had been trained by her own good mother, so that the Lady Terute had no cause for complaint against her.

The little Princess was very diligent, and her favorite studies were music and poetry. She would spend several hours practicing every day, and her father had the most proficient of masters he could find to teach her the koto (Japanese harp), the art of writing letters and verse. When she was twelve years of age she could play so beautifully that she and her step-mother were summoned to the Palace to perform before the Emperor.

It was the Festival of the Cherry Flowers, and there were great festivities at the Court. The Emperor threw himself into the enjoyment of the season, and commanded that Princess Hase should perform before him on the koto, and that her mother Princess Terute should accompany her on the flute.

The Emperor sat on a raised dais, before which was hung a curtain of finely-sliced bamboo and purple tassels, so that His Majesty might see all and not be seen, for no ordinary subject was allowed to look upon his sacred face.

Hase-Hime was a skilled musician though so young, and often astonished her masters by her wonderful memory and talent. On this momentous occasion she played well. But Princess Terute, her step-mother, who was a lazy woman and never took the trouble to practice daily, broke down in her accompaniment and had to request one of the Court ladies to take her place. This was a great disgrace, and she was furiously jealous to think that she had failed where her step-daughter succeeded; and to make matters worse the Emperor sent many beautiful gifts to the little Princess to reward her for playing so well at the Palace.

There was also now another reason why Princess Terute hated her step-daughter, for she had had the good fortune to have a son born to her, and in her inmost heart she kept saying:

"If only Hase-Hime were not here, my son would have all the love of his father."

And never having learned to control herself, she allowed this wicked thought to grow into the awful desire of taking her step-daughter's life.

So one day she secretly ordered some poison and poisoned some sweet wine. This poisoned wine she put into a bottle. Into another similar bottle she poured some good wine. It was the occasion of the Boys' Festival on the fifth of May, and Hase-Hime was playing with her little brother. All his toys of warriors and heroes were spread out and she was telling him wonderful stories about each of them. They were both enjoying themselves and laughing merrily with their attendants when his mother entered with the two bottles of wine and some delicious cakes.

"You are both so good and happy." said the wicked Princess Terute with a smile, "that I have brought you some sweet wine as a reward—and here are some nice cakes for my good children."

And she filled two cups from the different bottles.

Hase-Hime, never dreaming of the dreadful part her step-mother was acting, took one of the cups of wine and gave to her little step brother the other that had been poured out for him.

The wicked woman had carefully marked the poisoned bottle, but on coming into the room she had grown nervous, and pouring out the wine hurriedly had unconsciously given the poisoned cup to her own child. All this time she was anxiously watching the little Princess, but to her amazement no change whatever took place in the young girl's face. Suddenly the little boy screamed and threw himself on the floor, doubled up with pain. His mother flew to him, taking the precaution to upset the two tiny jars of wine which she had brought into the room, and lifted him up. The attendants rushed for the doctor, but nothing could save the child—he died within the hour in his mother's arms. Doctors did not know much in those ancient times, and it was thought that the wine had disagreed with the boy, causing convulsions of which he died.

Thus was the wicked woman punished in losing her own child when she had tried to do away with her step-daughter; but instead of blaming herself she began to hate Hase-Hime more than ever in the bitterness and wretchedness of her own heart, and she eagerly watched for an opportunity to do her harm, which was, however, long in coming.

When Hase-Hime was thirteen years of age, she had already become mentioned as a poetess of some merit. This was an accomplishment very much cultivated by the women of old Japan and one held in high esteem.

It was the rainy season at Nara, and floods were reported every day as doing damage in the neighborhood. The river Tatsuta, which flowed through the Imperial Palace grounds, was swollen to the top of its banks, and the roaring of the torrents of water rushing along a narrow bed so disturbed the

Emperor's rest day and night, that a serious nervous disorder was the result. An Imperial Edict was sent forth to all the Buddhist temples commanding the priests to offer up continuous prayers to Heaven to stop the noise of the flood. But this was of no avail.

Then it was whispered in Court circles that the Princess Hase, the daughter of Prince Toyonari Fujiwara, second minister at Court, was the most gifted poetess of the day, though still so young, and her masters confirmed the report. Long ago, a beautiful and gifted maiden-poetess had moved Heaven by praying in verse, had brought down rain upon a land famished with drought—so said the ancient biographers of the poetess Ono-no-Komachi. If the Princess Hase were to write a poem and offer it in prayer, might it not stop the noise of the rushing river and remove the cause of the Imperial illness? What the Court said at last reached the ears of the Emperor himself, and he sent an order to the minister Prince Toyonari to this effect.

Great indeed was Hase-Hime's fear and astonishment when her father sent for her and told her what was required of her. Heavy, indeed, was the duty that was laid on her young shoulders—that of saving the Emperor's life by the merit of her verse.

At last the day came and her poem was finished. It was written on a leaflet of paper heavily flecked with gold-dust. With her father and attendants and some of the Court officials, she proceeded to the bank of the roaring torrent and raising up her heart to Heaven, she read the poem she had composed, aloud, lifting it heavenwards in her two hands.

Strange indeed it seemed to all those standing round. The waters ceased their roaring, and the river was quiet in direct answer to her prayer. After this the Emperor soon recovered his health.

His Majesty was highly pleased, and sent for her to the Palace and rewarded her with the rank of Chinjo—that of Lieutenant-General—to distinguish her. From that time she was called Chinjo-hime, or the Lieutenant-General Princess, and respected and loved by all.

There was only one person who was not pleased at Hase-Hime's success. That one was her stepmother. Forever brooding over the death of her own child whom she had killed when trying to poison her step-daughter, she had the mortification of seeing her rise to power and honor, marked by Imperial favor and the admiration of the whole Court. Her envy and jealousy burned in her heart like fire. Many were the lies she carried to her husband about Hase-Hime, but all to no purpose. He would listen to none of her tales, telling her sharply that she was quite mistaken.

At last the step-mother, seizing the opportunity of her husband's absence, ordered one of her old servants to take the innocent girl to the Hibari Mountains, the wildest part of the country, and to kill her there. She invented a dreadful story about the little Princess, saying that this was the only way to prevent disgrace falling upon the family—by killing her.

Katoda, her vassal, was bound to obey his mistress. Anyhow, he saw that it would be the wisest plan to pretend obedience in the absence of the girl's father, so he placed Hase-Hime in a palanquin and accompanied her to the most solitary place he could find in the wild district. The poor child knew there was no good in protesting to her unkind step-mother at being sent away in this strange manner, so she went as she was told.

But the old servant knew that the young Princess was

quite innocent of all the things her step-mother had invented to him as reasons for her outrageous orders, and he determined to save her life. Unless he killed her, however, he could not return to his cruel task-mistress, so he decided to stay out in the wilderness. With the help of some peasants he soon built a little cottage, and having sent secretly for his wife to come, these two good old people did all in their power to take care of the now unfortunate Princess. She all the time trusted in her father, knowing that as soon as he returned home and found her absent, he would search for her.

Prince Toyonari, after some weeks, came home, and was told by his wife that his daughter Hime had done something wrong and had run away for fear of being punished. He was nearly ill with anxiety. Every one in the house told the same story—that Hase-Hime had suddenly disappeared, none of them knew why or whither. For fear of scandal he kept the matter quiet and searched everywhere he could think of, but all to no purpose.

One day, trying to forget his terrible worry, he called all his men together and told them to make ready for a several days' hunt in the mountains. They were soon ready and mounted, waiting at the gate for their lord. He rode hard and fast to the district of the Hibari Mountains, a great company following him. He was soon far ahead of every one, and at last found himself in a narrow picturesque valley.

Looking round and admiring the scenery, he noticed a tiny house on one of the hills quite near, and then he distinctly heard a beautiful clear voice reading aloud. Seized with curiosity as to who could be studying so diligently in such a lonely spot, he dismounted, and leaving his horse to his groom, he walked up the hillside and approached the cottage. As he drew nearer his surprise increased, for he could see that the reader was a beautiful girl. The cottage was wide open and she was sitting facing the view. Listening attentively, he heard her reading the Buddhist scriptures with great devotion. More and more curious, he hurried on to the tiny gate and entered the little garden, and looking up beheld his lost daughter Hase-Hime. She was so intent on what she was saying that she neither heard nor saw her father till he spoke.

"Hase-Hime!" he cried, "it is you, my Hase-Hime!"

Taken by surprise, she could hardly realize that it was her own dear father who was calling her, and for a moment she was utterly bereft of the power to speak or move.

"My father, my father! It is indeed you—oh, my father!" was all she could say, and running to him she caught hold of his thick sleeve, and burying her face burst into a passion of tears.

Her father stroked her dark hair, asking her gently to tell him all that had happened, but she only wept on, and he wondered if he were not really dreaming.

Then the faithful old servant Katoda came out, and bowing himself to the ground before his master, poured out the long tale of wrong, telling him all that had happened, and how it was that he found his daughter in such a wild and desolate spot with only two old servants to take care of her.

The Prince's astonishment and indignation knew no bounds. He gave up the hunt at once and hurried home with his daughter. One of the company galloped ahead to inform the household of the glad news, and the step-mother hearing what had happened, and fearful of meeting her husband now that her wickedness was discovered, fled from the house and returned in disgrace to her father's roof, and nothing more was heard of her.

The old servant Katoda was rewarded with the highest promotion in his master's service, and lived happily to the end of his days, devoted to the little Princess, who never forgot that she owed her life to this faithful retainer. She was no longer troubled by an unkind step-mother, and her days passed happily and quietly with her father.

As Prince Toyonari had no son, he adopted a younger son of one of the Court nobles to be his heir, and to marry his daughter Hase-Hime, and in a few years the marriage took place. Hase-Hime lived to a good old age, and all said that she was the wisest, most devout, and most beautiful mistress that had ever reigned in Prince Toyonari's ancient house. She had the joy of presenting her son, the future lord of the family, to her father just before he retired from active life.

To this day there is preserved a piece of needle-work in one of the Buddhist temples of Kioto. It is a beautiful piece of tapestry, with the figure of Buddha embroidered in the silky threads drawn from the stem of the lotus. This is said to have been the work of the hands of the good Princess Hase.

THE STORY OF THE MAN
WHO DID NOT WISH TO DIE

Long, long ago there lived a man called Sentaro. His surname meant "Millionaire," but although he was not so rich as all that, he was still very far removed from being poor. He had inherited a small fortune from his father and lived on this, spending his time carelessly, without any serious thoughts of work, till he was about thirty-two years of age.

One day, without any reason whatsoever, the thought of death and sickness came to him. The idea of falling ill or dying made him very wretched.

"I should like to live," he said to himself, "till I am five or six hundred years old at least, free from all sickness. The ordinary span of a man's life is very short."

He wondered whether it were possible, by living simply and frugally henceforth, to prolong his life as long as he wished.

He knew there were many stories in ancient history of emperors who had lived a thousand years, and there was a Princess of Yamato, who, it was said, lived to the age of five hundred. This was the latest story of a very long life record.

Sentaro had often heard the tale of the Chinese King named Shin-no-Shiko. He was one of the most able and powerful rulers in Chinese history. He built all the large palaces, and also the famous great wall of China. He had everything in the world he could wish for, but in spite of all his happiness and the luxury and the splendor of his Court, the wisdom of his councilors and the glory of his reign, he was miserable because he knew that one day he must die and leave it all.

When Shin-no-Shiko went to bed at night, when he rose

in the morning, as he went through his day, the thought of death was always with him. He could not get away from it. Ah—if only he could find the "Elixir of Life," he would be happy.

The Emperor at last called a meeting of his courtiers and asked them all if they could not find for him the "Elixir of Life" of which he had so often read and heard.

One old courtier, Jofuku by name, said that far away across the seas there was a country called Horaizan, and that certain hermits lived there who possessed the secret of the "Elixir of Life." Whoever drank of this wonderful draught lived forever.

The Emperor ordered Jofuku to set out for the land of Horaizan, to find the hermits, and to bring him back a phial of the magic elixir. He gave Jofuku one of his best junks, fitted it out for him, and loaded it with great quantities of treasures and precious stones for Jofuku to take as presents to the hermits.

Jofuku sailed for the land of Horaizan, but he never returned to the waiting Emperor; but ever since that time Mount Fuji has been said to be the fabled Horaizan and the home of hermits who had the secret of the elixir, and Jofuku has been worshiped as their patron god.

Now Sentaro determined to set out to find the hermits, and if he could, to become one, so that he might obtain the water of perpetual life. He remembered that as a child he had been told that not only did these hermits live on Mount Fuji, but that they were said to inhabit all the very high peaks.

So he left his old home to the care of his relatives, and started out on his quest. He traveled through all the mountainous regions of the land, climbing to the tops of the highest peaks, but never a hermit did he find.

At last, after wandering in an unknown region for many days, he met a hunter.

"Can you tell me," asked Sentaro, "where the hermits live who have the Elixir of Life?"

"No." said the hunter; "I can't tell you where such hermits live, but there is a notorious robber living in these parts. It is said that he is chief of a band of two hundred followers."

This odd answer irritated Sentaro very much, and he thought how foolish it was to waste more time in looking for the hermits in this way, so he decided to go at once to the shrine of Jofuku, who is worshiped as the patron god of the hermits in the south of Japan.

Sentaro reached the shrine and prayed for seven days, entreating Jofuku to show him the way to a hermit who could give him what he wanted so much to find.

At midnight of the seventh day, as Sentaro knelt in the temple, the door of the innermost shrine flew open, and Jofuku appeared in a luminous cloud, and calling to Sentaro to come nearer, spoke thus:

"Your desire is a very selfish one and cannot be easily granted. You think that you would like to become a hermit so as to find the Elixir of Life. Do you know how hard a hermit's life is? A hermit is only allowed to eat fruit and berries and the bark of pine trees; a hermit must cut himself off from the world so that his heart may become as pure as gold and free from every earthly desire. Gradually after following these strict rules, the hermit ceases to feel hunger or cold or heat, and his body becomes so light that he can ride on a crane or a carp, and can walk on water without getting his feet wet."

"You, Sentaro, are fond of good living and of every com-

fort. You are not even like an ordinary man, for you are excep-
tionally idle, and more sensitive to heat and cold than most
people. You would never be able to go barefoot or to wear only
one thin dress in the winter time! Do you think that you would
ever have the patience or the endurance to live a hermit's life?"

"In answer to your prayer, however, I will help you in
another way. I will send you to the country of Perpetual Life,
where death never comes—where the people live forever!"

Saying this, Jofuku put into Sentaro's hand a little crane
made of paper, telling him to sit on its back and it would carry
him there.

Sentaro obeyed wonderingly. The crane grew large
enough for him to ride on it with comfort. It then spread its
wings, rose high in the air, and flew away over the mountains
right out to sea.

Sentaro was at first quite frightened; but by degrees he
grew accustomed to the swift flight through the air. On and
on they went for thousands of miles. The bird never stopped
for rest or food, but as it was a paper bird it doubtless did
not require any nourishment, and strange to say, neither did
Sentaro.

After several days they reached an island. The crane flew
some distance inland and then alighted.

As soon as Sentaro got down from the bird's back, the
crane folded up of its own accord and flew into his pocket.

Now Sentaro began to look about him wonderingly, curious to see what the country of Perpetual Life was like. He
walked first round about the country and then through the
town. Everything was, of course, quite strange, and different
from his own land. But both the land and the people seemed
prosperous, so he decided that it would be good for him to

stay there and took up lodgings at one of the hotels.

The proprietor was a kind man, and when Sentaro told him that he was a stranger and had come to live there, he promised to arrange everything that was necessary with the governor of the city concerning Sentaro's sojourn there. He even found a house for his guest, and in this way Sentaro obtained his great wish and became a resident in the country of Perpetual Life.

Within the memory of all the islanders no man had ever died there, and sickness was a thing unknown. Priests had come over from India and China and told them of a beautiful country called Paradise, where happiness and bliss and contentment fill all men's hearts, but its gates could only be reached by dying. This tradition was handed down for ages from generation to generation—but none knew exactly what death was except that it led to Paradise.

Quite unlike Sentaro and other ordinary people, instead of having a great dread of death, they all, both rich and poor, longed for it as something good and desirable. They were all tired of their long, long lives, and longed to go to the happy land of contentment called Paradise of which the priests had told them centuries ago.

All this Sentaro soon found out by talking to the islanders. He found himself, according to his ideas, in the land of Topsyturvydom. Everything was upside down. He had wished to escape from dying. He had come to the land of Perpetual Life with great relief and joy, only to find that the inhabitants themselves, doomed never to die, would consider it bliss to find death.

What he had hitherto considered poison these people ate as good food, and all the things to which he had been accustomed as food they rejected. Whenever any merchants from other countries arrived, the rich people rushed to them eager to buy poisons. These they swallowed eagerly, hoping for death to come so that they might go to Paradise.

But what were deadly poisons in other lands were without effect in this strange place, and people who swallowed them with the hope of dying, only found that in a short time they felt better in health instead of worse.

Vainly they tried to imagine what death could be like. The wealthy would have given all their money and all their goods if they could but shorten their lives to two or three hundred years even. Without any change to live on forever seemed to this people wearisome and sad.

In the chemist shops there was a drug which was in constant demand, because after using it for a hundred years, it was supposed to turn the hair slightly gray and to bring about disorders of the stomach.

Sentaro was astonished to find that the poisonous globe-fish was served up in restaurants as a delectable dish, and hawkers in the streets went about selling sauces made of Spanish flies. He never saw any one ill after eating these horrible things, nor did he ever see any one with as much as a cold.

Sentaro was delighted. He said to himself that he would never grow tired of living, and that he considered it profane to wish for death. He was the only happy man on the island. For his part he wished to live thousands of years and to enjoy life. He set himself up in business, and for the present never even dreamed of going back to his native land.

As years went by, however, things did not go as smoothly as at first. He had heavy losses in business, and several times some affairs went wrong with his neighbors. This caused him great annoyance.

Time passed like the flight of an arrow for him, for he was busy from morning till night. Three hundred years went by in this monotonous way, and then at last he began to grow tired of life in this country, and he longed to see his own land and his old home. However long he lived here, life would always be the same, so was it not foolish and wearisome to stay on here forever?

Sentaro, in his wish to escape from the country of Perpetual Life, recollected Jofuku, who had helped him before when he was wishing to escape from death—and he prayed to the saint to bring him back to his own land again.

No sooner did he pray than the paper crane popped out of his pocket. Sentaro was amazed to see that it had remained undamaged after all these years. Once more the bird grew and grew till it was large enough for him to mount it. As he did so, the bird spread its wings and flew, swiftly out across the sea in the direction of Japan.

Such was the willfulness of the man's nature that he looked back and regretted all he had left behind. He tried to stop the bird in vain. The crane held on its way for thousands of miles across the ocean.

Then a storm came on, and the wonderful paper crane got damp, crumpled up, and fell into the sea. Sentaro fell with it. Very much frightened at the thought of being drowned, he cried out loudly to Jofuku to save him. He looked round, but there was no ship in sight. He swallowed a quantity of sea-water, which only increased his miserable plight. While he was thus struggling to keep himself afloat, he saw a monstrous shark swimming towards him. As it came nearer it opened its huge mouth ready to devour him. Sentaro was all but paralyzed with fear now that he felt his end so near, and screamed out as loudly as ever he could to Jofuku to come and rescue him.

Lo, and behold, Sentaro was awakened by his own screams, to find that during his long prayer he had fallen asleep before the shrine, and that all his extraordinary and frightful adventures had been only a wild dream. He was in a cold perspiration with fright, and utterly bewildered.

Suddenly a bright light came towards him, and in the light stood a messenger. The messenger held a book in his hand, and spoke to Sentaro:

"I am sent to you by Jofuku, who in answer to your prayer, has permitted you in a dream to see the land of Perpetual Life. But you grew weary of living there, and begged to be allowed to return to your native land so that you might die. Jofuku, so that he might try you, allowed you to drop into the sea, and then sent a shark to swallow you up. Your desire for death was not real, for even at that moment you cried out loudly and shouted for help."

"It is also vain for you to wish to become a hermit, or to find the Elixir of Life. These things are not for such as you—your life is not austere enough. It is best for you to go back to your paternal home, and to live a good and industrious life. Never neglect to keep the anniversaries of your ancestors, and make it your duty to provide for your children's future. Thus will you live to a good old age and be happy, but give up the vain desire to escape death, for no man can do that, and by this time you have surely found out that even when selfish desires are granted they do not bring happiness."

"In this book I give you there are many precepts good for you to know—if you study them, you will be guided in the way

I have pointed out to you."

The angel disappeared as soon as he had finished speaking, and Sentaro took the lesson to heart. With the book in his hand he returned to his old home, and giving up all his old vain wishes, tried to live a good and useful life and to observe the lessons taught him in the book, and he and his house prospered henceforth.

THE BAMBOO-CUTTER AND THE MOON-CHILD

Long, long ago, there lived an old bamboo wood-cutter. He was very poor and sad also, for no child had Heaven sent to cheer his old age, and in his heart there was no hope of rest from work till he died and was laid in the quiet grave. Every morning he went forth into the woods and hills wherever the bamboo reared its lithe green plumes against the sky. When he had made his choice, he would cut down these feathers of the forest, and splitting them lengthwise, or cutting them into joints, would carry the bamboo wood home and make it into various articles for the household, and he and his old wife gained a small livelihood by selling them.

One morning as usual he had gone out to his work, and having found a nice clump of bamboos, had set to work to cut some of them down. Suddenly the green grove of bamboos was flooded with a bright soft light, as if the full moon had risen over the spot. Looking round in astonishment, he saw that the brilliance was streaming from one bamboo. The old man, full of wonder, dropped his ax and went towards the light. On nearer approach he saw that this soft splendor came from a hollow in the green bamboo stem, and still more wonderful to behold, in the midst of the brilliance stood a tiny human being, only three inches in height, and exquisitely beautiful in appearance.

"You must be sent to be my child, for I find you here among the bamboos where lies my daily work," said the old man, and taking the little creature in his hand he took it home to his wife to bring up. The tiny girl was so exceedingly beautiful and so small, that the old woman put her into a basket to safeguard her from the least possibility of being hurt in any way.

The old couple were now very happy, for it had been a lifelong regret that they had no children of their own, and with joy they now expended all the love of their old age on the little child who had come to them in so marvelous a manner.

From this time on, the old man often found gold in the notches of the bamboos when he hewed them down and cut them up; not only gold, but precious stones also, so that by degrees he became rich. He built himself a fine house, and was no longer known as the poor bamboo woodcutter, but as a wealthy man.

Three months passed quickly away, and in that time the bamboo child had, wonderful to say, become a full-grown girl, so her foster-parents did up her hair and dressed her in beautiful kimonos. She was of such wondrous beauty that they placed her behind the screens like a princess, and allowed no one to see her, waiting upon her themselves. It seemed as if she were made of light, for the house was filled with a soft shining, so that even in the dark of night it was like daytime. Her presence seemed to have a benign influence on those there. Whenever the old man felt sad, he had only to look upon his foster-daughter and his sorrow vanished, and he became as happy as when he was a youth.

At last the day came for the naming of their new-found child, so the old couple called in a celebrated name-giver, and he gave her the name of Princess Moonlight, because her body gave forth so much soft bright light that she might have been a daughter of the Moon God.

For three days the festival was kept up with song and dance and music. All the friends and relations of the old couple were present, and great was their enjoyment of the festivities held to celebrate the naming of Princess Moonlight. Everyone who saw her declared that there never had been seen any one so lovely; all the beauties throughout the length and breadth of the land would grow pale beside her, so they said. The fame of the Princess's loveliness spread far and wide, and many were the suitors who desired to win her hand, or even so much as to see her.

Suitors from far and near posted themselves outside the house, and made little holes in the fence, in the hope of catching a glimpse of the Princess as she went from one room to the other along the veranda. They stayed there day and night, sacrificing even their sleep for a chance of seeing her, but all in vain. Then they approached the house, and tried to speak to the old man and his wife or some of the servants, but not even this was granted them.

Still, in spite of all this disappointment they stayed on day after day, and night after night, and counted it as nothing, so great was their desire to see the Princess.

At last, however, most of the men, seeing how hopeless their quest was, lost heart and hope both, and returned to their homes. All except five Knights, whose ardor and determination, instead of waning, seemed to wax greater with obstacles. These five men even went without their meals, and took snatches of whatever they could get brought to them, so that they might always stand outside the dwelling. They stood there in all weathers, in sunshine and in rain.

Sometimes they wrote letters to the Princess, but no answer was vouchsafed to them. Then when letters failed to draw any reply, they wrote poems to her telling her of the hopeless love which kept them from sleep, from food, from rest, and even from their homes. Still Princes Moonlight gave no sign of having received their verses.

In this hopeless state the winter passed. The snow and frost and the cold winds gradually gave place to the gentle warmth of spring. Then the summer came, and the sun burned white and scorching in the heavens above and on the earth beneath, and still these faithful Knights kept watch and waited. At the end of these long months they called out to the old bamboo-cutter and entreated him to have some mercy upon them and to show them the Princess, but he answered only that as he was not her real father he could not insist on her obeying him against her wishes.

The five Knights on receiving this stern answer returned to their several homes, and pondered over the best means of touching the proud Princess's heart, even so much as to grant them a hearing. They took their rosaries in hand and knelt before their household shrines, and burned precious incense, praying to Buddha to give them their heart's desire. Thus several days passed, but even so they could not rest in their homes.

So again they set out for the bamboo-cutter's house. This time the old man came out to see them, and they asked him to let them know if it was the Princess's resolution never to see any man whatsoever, and they implored him to speak for them and to tell her the greatness of their love, and how long they had waited through the cold of winter and the heat of summer, sleepless and roofless through all weathers, without food and without rest, in the ardent hope of winning her, and they were willing to consider this long vigil as pleasure if she would but give them one chance of pleading their cause with her.

The old man lent a willing ear to their tale of love, for in his inmost heart he felt sorry for these faithful suitors and would have liked to see his lovely foster-daughter married to one of them. So he went in to Princess Moonlight and said reverently:

"Although you have always seemed to me to be a heavenly being, yet I have had the trouble of bringing you up as my own child and you have been glad of the protection of my roof. Will you refuse to do as I wish?"

Then Princess Moonlight replied that there was nothing she would not do for him, that she honored and loved him as her own father, and that as for herself she could not remember the time before she came to earth.

The old man listened with great joy as she spoke these dutiful words. Then he told her how anxious he was to see her safely and happily married before he died.

"I am an old man, over seventy years of age, and my end may come any time now. It is necessary and right that you should see these five suitors and choose one of them."

"Oh, why," said the Princess in distress, "must I do this? I have no wish to marry now."

"I found you," answered the old man, "many years ago, when you were a little creature three inches high, in the midst of a great white light. The light streamed from the bamboo in which you were hid and led me to you. So I have always thought that you were more than mortal woman. While I am alive it is right for you to remain as you are if you wish to do so, but some day I shall cease to be and who will take care of you then? Therefore I pray you to meet these five brave men one at a time and make up your mind to marry one of them!"

Then the Princess answered that she felt sure that she

was not as beautiful as perhaps report made her out to be, and that even if she consented to marry any one of them, not really knowing her before, his heart might change afterwards. So as she did not feel sure of them, even though her father told her they were worthy Knights, she did not feel it wise to see them.

"All you say is very reasonable," said the old man, "but what kind of men will you consent to see? I do not call these five men who have waited on you for months, light-hearted. They have stood outside this house through the winter and the summer, often denying themselves food and sleep so that they may win you. What more can you demand?"

Then Princess Moonlight said she must make further trial of their love before she would grant their request to interview her. The five warriors were to prove their love by each bringing her from distant countries something that she desired to possess.

That same evening the suitors arrived and began to play their flutes in turn, and to sing their self-composed songs telling of their great and tireless love. The bamboo-cutter went out to them and offered them his sympathy for all they had endured and all the patience they had shown in their desire to win his foster-daughter. Then he gave them her message, that she would consent to marry whosoever was successful in bringing her what she wanted. This was to test them.

The five all accepted the trial, and thought it an excellent plan, for it would prevent jealousy between them.

Princess Moonlight then sent word to the First Knight that she requested him to bring her the stone bowl which had belonged to Buddha in India.

The Second Knight was asked to go to the Mountain of Horai, said to be situated in the Eastern Sea, and to bring her a branch of the wonderful tree that grew on its summit. The roots of this tree were of silver, the trunk of gold, and the branches bore as fruit white jewels.

The Third Knight was told to go to China and search for the fire-rat and to bring her its skin.

The Fourth Knight was told to search for the dragon that carried on its head the stone radiating five colors and to bring the stone to her.

The Fifth Knight was to find the swallow which carried a shell in its stomach and to bring the shell to her.

The old man thought these very hard tasks and hesitated to carry the messages, but the Princess would make no other conditions. So her commands were issued word for word to the five men who, when they heard what was required of them, were all disheartened and disgusted at what seemed to them the impossibility of the tasks given them and returned to their own homes in despair.

But after a time, when they thought of the Princess, the love in their hearts revived for her, and they resolved to make an attempt to get what she desired of them.

The First Knight sent word to the Princess that he was starting out that day on the quest of Buddha's bowl, and he hoped soon to bring it to her. But he had not the courage to go all the way to India, for in those days traveling was very difficult and full of danger, so he went to one of the temples in Kyoto and took a stone bowl from the altar there, paying the priest a large sum of money for it. He then wrapped it in a cloth of gold and, waiting quietly for three years, returned and carried it to the old man.

Princess Moonlight wondered that the Knight should have returned so soon. She took the bowl from its gold wrapping, expecting it to make the room full of light, but it did not shine at all, so she knew that it was a sham thing and not the true bowl of Buddha. She returned it at once and refused to see him. The Knight threw the bowl away and returned to his home in despair. He gave up now all hopes of ever winning the Princess.

The Second Knight told his parents that he needed change of air for his health, for he was ashamed to tell them that love for the Princess Moonlight was the real cause of his leaving them. He then left his home, at the same time sending word to the Princess that he was setting out for Mount Horai in the hope of getting her a branch of the gold and silver tree which she so much wished to have. He only allowed his servants to accompany him half-way, and then sent them back. He reached the seashore and embarked on a small ship, and after sailing away for three days he landed and employed several carpenters to build him a house contrived in such a way that no one could get access to it. He then shut himself up with six skilled jewelers, and endeavored to make such a gold and silver branch as he thought would satisfy the Princess as having come from the wonderful tree growing on Mount Horai. Every one whom he had asked declared that Mount Horai belonged to the land of fable and not to fact.

When the branch was finished, he took his journey home and tried to make himself look as if he were wearied and worn out with travel. He put the jeweled branch into a lacquer box and carried it to the bamboo-cutter, begging him to present it to the Princess.

The old man was quite deceived by the travel-stained appearance of the Knight, and thought that he had only just returned from his long journey with the branch. So he tried to persuade the Princess to consent to see the man. But she remained silent and looked very sad. The old man began to take out the branch and praised it as a wonderful treasure to be found nowhere in the whole land. Then he spoke of the Knight, how handsome and how brave he was to have undertaken a journey to so remote a place as the Mount of Horai.

Princess Moonlight took the branch in her hand and looked at it carefully. She then told her foster-parent that she knew it was impossible for the man to have obtained a branch from the gold and silver tree growing on Mount Horai so quickly or so easily, and she was sorry to say she believed it artificial.

The old man then went out to the expectant Knight, who had now approached the house, and asked where he had found the branch. Then the man did not scruple to make up a long story.

"Two years ago I took a ship and started in search of Mount Horai. After going before the wind for some time I reached the far Eastern Sea. Then a great storm arose and I was tossed about for many days, losing all count of the points of the compass, and finally we were blown ashore on an unknown island. Here I found the place inhabited by demons who at one time threatened to kill and eat me. However, I managed to make friends with these horrible creatures, and they helped me and my sailors to repair the boat, and I set sail again. Our food gave out, and we suffered much from sickness on board. At last, on the five-hundredth day from the day of starting, I saw far off on the horizon what looked like the peak of a mountain. On nearer approach, this proved to be an island, in the center of which rose a high mountain. I landed, and after wandering about for two or three days, I saw a shining being coming towards me on the beach, holding in his hands a golden bowl. I went up to him and asked him if I had, by good chance, found the island of Mount Horai, and he answered:"

"'Yes, this is Mount Horai!'"

"With much difficulty I climbed to the summit, here stood the golden tree growing with silver roots in the ground. The wonders of that strange land are many, and if I began to tell you about them I could never stop. In spite of my wish to stay there long, on breaking off the branch I hurried back. With utmost speed it has taken me four hundred days to get back, and, as you see, my clothes are still damp from exposure on the long sea voyage. I have not even waited to change my raiment, so anxious was I to bring the branch to the Princess quickly."

Just at this moment the six jewelers, who had been employed on the making of the branch, but not yet paid by the Knight, arrived at the house and sent in a petition to the Princess to be paid for their labor. They said that they had worked for over a thousand days making the branch of gold, with its silver twigs and its jeweled fruit, that was now presented to her by the Knight, but as yet they had received nothing in payment. So this Knight's deception was thus found out, and the Princess, glad of an escape from one more importunate suitor, was only too pleased to send back the branch. She called in the workmen and had them paid liberally, and they went away happy. But on the way home they were overtaken by the disappointed man, who beat them till they were nearly dead, for letting out the secret, and they barely escaped with their lives. The Knight then returned home, raging in his heart; and in despair of ever winning the Princess gave up society and retired to a solitary life among the mountains.

Now the Third Knight had a friend in China, so he wrote to him to get the skin of the fire-rat. The virtue of any part of this animal was that no fire could harm it. He promised his friend any amount of money he liked to ask if only he could get him the desired article. As soon as the news came that the ship on which his friend had sailed home had come into port, he rode seven days on horseback to meet him. He handed his friend a large sum of money, and received the fire-rat's skin. When he reached home he put it carefully in a box and sent it in to the Princess while he waited outside for her answer.

The bamboo-cutter took the box from the Knight and, as usual, carried it in to her and tried to coax her to see the Knight at once, but Princess Moonlight refused, saying that she must first put the skin to test by putting it into the fire. If it were the real thing it would not burn. So she took off the crape wrapper and opened the box, and then threw the skin into the fire. The skin crackled and burnt up at once, and the Princess knew that this man also had not fulfilled his word. So the Third Knight failed also.

Now the Fourth Knight was no more enterprising than the rest. Instead of starting out on the quest of the dragon bearing on its head the five-color-radiating jewel, he called all his servants together and gave them the order to seek for it far and wide in Japan and in China, and he strictly forbade any of them to return till they had found it.

His numerous retainers and servants started out in different directions, with no intention, however, of obeying what they considered an impossible order. They simply took a holiday, went to pleasant country places together, and grumbled at their master's unreasonableness.

The Knight meanwhile, thinking that his retainers could not fail to find the jewel, repaired to his house, and fitted it up beautifully for the reception of the Princess, he felt so sure of winning her.

One year passed away in weary waiting, and still his men did not return with the dragon-jewel. The Knight became desperate. He could wait no longer, so taking with him only two men he hired a ship and commanded the captain to go in search of the dragon; the captain and the sailors refused to undertake what they said was an absurd search, but the Knight compelled them at last to put out to sea.

When they had been but a few days out they encountered a great storm which lasted so long that, by the time its fury abated, the Knight had determined to give up the hunt of the dragon. They were at last blown on shore, for navigation was primitive in those days. Worn out with his travels and anxiety, the fourth suitor gave himself up to rest. He had caught a very heavy cold, and had to go to bed with a swollen face.

The governor of the place, hearing of his plight, sent messengers with a letter inviting him to his house. While he was there thinking over all his troubles, his love for the Princess turned to anger, and he blamed her for all the hardships he had undergone. He thought that it was quite probable she had wished to kill him so that she might be rid of him, and in order to carry out her wish had sent him upon his impossible quest.

At this point all the servants he had sent out to find the jewel came to see him, and were surprised to find praise instead of displeasure awaiting them. Their master told them that he was heartily sick of adventure, and said that he never intended to go near the Princess's house again in the future.

Like all the rest, the Fifth Knight failed in his quest—he could not find the swallow's shell.

By this time the fame of Princess Moonlight's beauty had reached the ears of the Emperor, and he sent one of the Court ladies to see if she were really as lovely as report said; if so he would summon her to the Palace and make her one of the ladies-in-waiting.

When the Court lady arrived, in spite of her father's entreaties, Princess Moonlight refused to see her. The Imperial messenger insisted, saying it was the Emperor's order. Then Princess Moonlight told the old man that if she was forced to go to the Palace in obedience to the Emperor's order, she would vanish from the earth.

When the Emperor was told of her persistence in refusing to obey his summons, and that if pressed to obey she would disappear altogether from sight, he determined to go and see her. So he planned to go on a hunting excursion in the neighborhood of the bamboo-cutter's house, and see the Princess himself. He sent word to the old man of his intention, and he received consent to the scheme. The next day the Emperor set out with his retinue, which he soon managed to outride. He found the bamboo-cutter's house and dismounted. He then entered the house and went straight to where the Princess was sitting with her attendant maidens.

Never had he seen any one so wonderfully beautiful, and he could not but look at her, for she was more lovely than any human being as she shone in her own soft radiance. When Princess Moonlight became aware that a stranger was looking at her she tried to escape from the room, but the Emperor caught her and begged her to listen to what he had to say. Her only answer was to hide her face in her sleeves.

The Emperor fell deeply in love with her, and begged her to come to the Court, where he would give her a position of honor and everything she could wish for. He was about to send for one of the Imperial palanquins to take her back with him at once, saying that her grace and beauty should adorn a Court, and not be hidden in a bamboo-cutter's cottage.

But the Princess stopped him. She said that if she were forced to go to the Palace she would turn at once into a shadow, and even as she spoke she began to lose her form. Her figure faded from his sight while he looked.

The Emperor then promised to leave her free if only she would resume her former shape, which she did.

It was now time for him to return, for his retinue would be wondering what had happened to their Royal master when they missed him for so long. So he bade her good-by, and left the house with a sad heart. Princess Moonlight was for him the most beautiful woman in the world; all others were dark beside her, and he thought of her night and day. His Majesty now spent much of his time in writing poems, telling her of his love and devotion, and sent them to her, and though she refused to see him again she answered with many verses of her own composing, which told him gently and kindly that she could never marry any one on this earth. These little songs always gave him pleasure.

At this time her foster-parents noticed that night after night the Princess would sit on her balcony and gaze for hours at the moon, in a spirit of the deepest dejection, ending always in a burst of tears. One night the old man found her thus weeping as if her heart were broken, and he besought her to tell him the reason of her sorrow.

With many tears she told him that he had guessed rightly

when he supposed her not to belong to this world—that she had in truth come from the moon, and that her time on earth would soon be over. On the fifteenth day of that very month of August her friends from the moon would come to fetch her, and she would have to return. Her parents were both there, but having spent a lifetime on the earth she had forgotten them, and also the moon-world to which she belonged. It made her weep, she said, to think of leaving her kind foster-parents, and the home where she had been happy for so long.

When her attendants heard this they were very sad, and could not eat or drink for sadness at the thought that the Princess was so soon to leave them.

The Emperor, as soon as the news was carried to him, sent messengers to the house to find out if the report were true or not.

The old bamboo-cutter went out to meet the Imperial messengers. The last few days of sorrow had told upon the old man; he had aged greatly, and looked much more than his seventy years. Weeping bitterly, he told them that the report was only too true, but he intended, however, to make prisoners of the envoys from the moon, and to do all he could to prevent the Princess from being carried back.

The men returned and told His Majesty all that had passed. On the fifteenth day of that month the Emperor sent a guard of two thousand warriors to watch the house. One thousand stationed themselves on the roof, another thousand kept watch round all the entrances of the house. All were well trained archers, with bows and arrows. The bamboo-cutter and his wife hid Princess Moonlight in an inner room.

The old man gave orders that no one was to sleep that night, all in the house were to keep a strict watch, and be ready to protect the Princess. With these precautions, and the help of the Emperor's men-at-arms, he hoped to withstand the moon-messengers, but the Princess told him that all these measures to keep her would be useless, and that when her people came for her nothing whatever could prevent them from carrying out their purpose. Even the Emperors men would be powerless. Then she added with tears that she was very, very sorry to leave him and his wife, whom she had learned to love as her parents, that if she could do as she liked she would stay with them in their old age, and try to make some return for all the love and kindness they had showered upon her during all her earthly life.

The night wore on! The yellow harvest moon rose high in the heavens, flooding the world asleep with her golden light. Silence reigned over the pine and the bamboo forests, and on the roof where the thousand men-at-arms waited.

Then the night grew gray towards the dawn and all hoped that the danger was over—that Princess Moonlight would not have to leave them after all. Then suddenly the watchers saw a cloud form round the moon—and while they looked this cloud began to roll earthwards. Nearer and nearer it came, and every one saw with dismay that its course lay towards the house.

In a short time the sky was entirely obscured, till at last the cloud lay over the dwelling only ten feet off the ground. In the midst of the cloud there stood a flying chariot, and in the chariot a band of luminous beings. One amongst them who looked like a king and appeared to be the chief stepped out of the chariot, and, poised in air, called to the old man to come out.

"The time has come," he said, "for Princess Moonlight to return to the moon from whence she came. She committed a grave fault, and as a punishment was sent to live down here for a time. We know what good care you have taken of the Princess, and we have rewarded you for this and have sent you wealth and prosperity. We put the gold in the bamboos for you to find."

"I have brought up this Princess for twenty years and never once has she done a wrong thing, therefore the lady you are seeking cannot be this one," said the old man. "I pray you to lock elsewhere."

Then the messenger called aloud, saying:

"Princess Moonlight, come out from this lowly dwelling. Rest not here another moment."

At these words the screens of the Princess's room slid open of their own accord, revealing the Princess shining in her own radiance, bright and wonderful and full of beauty.

The messenger led her forth and placed her in the chariot. She looked back, and saw with pity the deep sorrow of the old man. She spoke to him many comforting words, and told him that it was not her will to leave him and that he must always think of her when looking at the moon.

The bamboo-cutter implored to be allowed to accompany her, but this was not allowed. The Princess took off her embroidered outer garment and gave it to him as a keepsake.

One of the moon beings in the chariot held a wonderful coat of wings, another had a phial full of the Elixir of Life which was given the Princess to drink. She swallowed a little and was about to give the rest to the old man, but she was prevented from doing so.

The robe of wings was about to be put upon her shoulders, but she said:

"Wait a little. I must not forget my good friend the Emperor. I must write him once more to say good-by while still in this human form."

In spite of the impatience of the messengers and charioteers she kept them waiting while she wrote. She placed the phial of the Elixir of Life with the letter, and, giving them to the old man, she asked him to deliver them to the Emperor.

Then the chariot began to roll heavenwards towards the moon, and as they all gazed with tearful eyes at the receding Princess, the dawn broke, and in the rosy light of day the moon-chariot and all in it were lost amongst the fleecy clouds that were now wafted across the sky on the wings of the morning wind.

Princess Moonlight's letter was carried to the Palace. His Majesty was afraid to touch the Elixir of Life, so he sent it with the letter to the top of the most sacred mountain in the land. Mount Fuji, and there the Royal emissaries burnt it on the summit at sunrise. So to this day people say there is smoke to be seen rising from the top of Mount Fuji to the clouds.

THE MIRROR OF MATSUYAMA

Long years ago in old Japan there lived in the Province of Echigo, a very remote part of Japan even in these days, a man and his wife. When this story begins they had been married for some years and were blessed with one little daughter. She was the joy and pride of both their lives, and in her they stored an endless source of happiness for their old age.

What golden letter days in their memory were these that had marked her growing up from babyhood; the visit to the temple when she was just thirty days old, her proud mother carrying her, robed in ceremonial kimono, to be put under the patronage of the family's household god; then her first dolls festival, when her parents gave her a set of dolls and their miniature belongings, to be added to as year succeeded year; and perhaps the most important occasion of all, on her third birthday, when her first OBI (broad brocade sash) of scarlet and gold was tied round her small waist, a sign that she had crossed the threshold of girlhood and left infancy behind. Now that she was seven years of age, and had learned to talk and to wait upon her parents in those several little ways so dear to the hearts of fond parents, their cup of happiness seemed full. There could not be found in the whole of the Island Empire a happier little family.

One day there was much excitement in the home, for the father had been suddenly summoned to the capital on business. In these days of railways and jinrickshas and other rapid modes of traveling, it is difficult to realize what such a journey as that from Matsuyama to Kyoto meant. The roads were rough and bad, and ordinary people had to walk every step of the way, whether the distance were one hundred or several hundred miles. Indeed, in those days it was as great an undertaking to go up to the capital as it is for a Japanese to make a voyage to Europe now.

So the wife was very anxious while she helped her husband get ready for the long journey, knowing what an arduous task lay before him. Vainly she wished that she could accompany him, but the distance was too great for the mother and child to go, and besides that, it was the wife's duty to take care of the home.

All was ready at last, and the husband stood in the porch with his little family round him.

"Do not be anxious, I will come back soon," said the man. "While I am away take care of everything, and especially of our little daughter."

"Yes, we shall be all right—but you—you must take care of yourself and delay not a day in coming back to us," said the wife, while the tears fell like rain from her eyes.

The little girl was the only one to smile, for she was ignorant of the sorrow of parting, and did not know that going to the capital was at all different from walking to the next village, which her father did very often. She ran to his side, and caught hold of his long sleeve to keep him a moment.

"Father, I will be very good while I am waiting for you to come back, so please bring me a present."

As the father turned to take a last look at his weeping wife and smiling, eager child, he felt as if some one were pulling him back by the hair, so hard was it for him to leave them behind, for they had never been separated before. But he knew that he must go, for the call was imperative. With a great effort he ceased to think, and resolutely turning away he went quickly down the little garden and out through the gate. His wife, catching up the child in her arms, ran as far as the gate, and watched him as he went down the road between the pines till he was lost in the haze of the distance and all she could see was his quaint peaked hat, and at last that vanished too.

"Now father has gone, you and I must take care of everything till he comes back," said the mother, as she made her way back to the house.

"Yes, I will be very good," said the child, nodding her head, "and when father comes home please tell him how good I have been, and then perhaps he will give me a present."

"Father is sure to bring you something that you want very much. I know, for I asked him to bring you a doll. You must think of father every day, and pray for a safe journey till he comes back."

"O, yes, when he comes home again how happy I shall be," said the child, clapping her hands, and her face growing bright with joy at the glad thought. It seemed to the mother as she looked at the child's face that her love for her grew deeper and deeper.

Then she set to work to make the winter clothes for the three of them. She set up her simple wooden spinning-wheel and spun the thread before she began to weave the stuffs. In the intervals of her work she directed the little girl's games and taught her to read the old stories of her country. Thus did the wife find consolation in work during the lonely days of her husband's absence. While the time was thus slipping quickly by in the quiet home, the husband finished his business and returned.

It would have been difficult for any one who did not know the man well to recognize him. He had traveled day after day, exposed to all weathers, for about a month altogether, and was sunburnt to bronze, but his fond wife and child knew him at a glance, and flew to meet him from either side, each catching hold of one of his sleeves in their eager greeting. Both the man and his wife rejoiced to find each other well. It seemed a very long time to all till—the mother and child helping—his straw sandals were untied, his large umbrella hat taken off, and he was again in their midst in the old familiar sitting-room that had been so empty while he was away.

As soon as they had sat down on the white mats, the father opened a bamboo basket that he had brought in with him, and took out a beautiful doll and a lacquer box full of cakes.

"Here," he said to the little girl, "is a present for you. It is a prize for taking care of mother and the house so well while I was away."

"Thank you," said the child, as she bowed her head to the ground, and then put out her hand just like a little maple leaf with its eager wide-spread fingers to take the doll and the box, both of which, coming from the capital, were prettier than anything she had ever seen. No words can tell how delighted the little girl was—her face seemed as if it would melt with joy, and she had no eyes and no thought for anything else.

Again the husband dived into the basket, and brought out this time a square wooden box, carefully tied up with red and white string, and handing it to his wife, said:

"And this is for you."

The wife took the box, and opening it carefully took out a metal disk with a handle attached. One side was bright and shining like a crystal, and the other was covered with raised figures of pine-trees and storks, which had been carved out of its smooth surface in lifelike reality. Never had she seen such a thing in her life, for she had been born and bred in the rural province of Echigo. She gazed into the shining disk, and looking up with surprise and wonder pictured on her face, she said:

"I see somebody looking at me in this round thing! What is it that you have given me?"

The husband laughed and said:

"Why, it is your own face that you see. What I have brought you is called a mirror, and whoever looks into its clear surface can see their own form reflected there. Although there are none to be found in this out of the way place, yet they have been in use in the capital from the most ancient times. There the mirror is considered a very necessary requisite for a woman to possess. There is an old proverb that 'As the sword is the soul of a samurai, so is the mirror the soul of a woman,' and according to popular tradition, a woman's mirror is an index to her own heart—if she keeps it bright and clear, so is her heart pure and good. It is also one of the treasures that form the insignia of the Emperor. So you must lay great store by your mirror, and use it carefully."

The wife listened to all her husband told her, and was pleased at learning so much that was new to her. She was still more pleased at the precious gift—his token of remembrance while he had been away.

"If the mirror represents my soul, I shall certainly treasure it as a valuable possession, and never will I use it carelessly." Saying so, she lifted it as high as her forehead, in grateful acknowledgment of the gift, and then shut it up in its box and put it away.

The wife saw that her husband was very tired, and set about serving the evening meal and making everything as comfortable as she could for him. It seemed to the little family as if they had not known what true happiness was before, so glad were they to be together again, and this evening the father had much to tell of his journey and of all he had seen at the great capital.

Time passed away in the peaceful home, and the parents saw their fondest hopes realized as their daughter grew from childhood into a beautiful girl of sixteen. As a gem of priceless value is held in its proud owner's hand, so had they reared her with unceasing love and care: and now their pains were more than doubly rewarded. What a comfort she was to her mother as she went about the house taking her part in the housekeeping, and how proud her father was of her, for she daily reminded him of her mother when he had first married her.

But, alas! in this world nothing lasts forever. Even the moon is not always perfect in shape, but loses its roundness with time, and flowers bloom and then fade. So at last the happiness of this family was broken up by a great sorrow. The good and gentle wife and mother was one day taken ill.

In the first days of her illness the father and daughter thought that it was only a cold, and were not particularly anxious. But the days went by and still the mother did not get better; she only grew worse, and the doctor was puzzled, for in spite of all he did the poor woman grew weaker day by day. The father and daughter were stricken with grief, and day or night the girl never left her mother's side. But in spite of all their efforts the woman's life was not to be saved.

One day as the girl sat near her mother's bed, trying to hide with a cheery smile the gnawing trouble at her heart, the mother roused herself and taking her daughter's hand, gazed earnestly and lovingly into her eyes. Her breath was labored and she spoke with difficulty:

"My daughter. I am sure that nothing can save me now. When I am dead, promise me to take care of your dear father and to try to be a good and dutiful woman."

"Oh, mother," said the girl as the tears rushed to her eyes, "you must not say such things. All you have to do is to make haste and get well—that will bring the greatest happiness to father and myself."

"Yes, I know, and it is a comfort to me in my last days to know how greatly you long for me to get better, but it is not to be. Do not look so sorrowful, for it was so ordained in my previous state of existence that I should die in this life just at this time; knowing this, I am quite resigned to my fate. And now I have something to give you whereby to remember me when I am gone."

Putting her hand out, she took from the side of the pillow a square wooden box tied up with a silken cord and tassels. Undoing this very carefully, she took out of the box the mirror that her husband had given her years ago.

"When you were still a little child your father went up to the capital and brought me back as a present this treasure; it is called a mirror. This I give you before I die. If, after I have ceased to be in this life, you are lonely and long to see me sometimes, then take out this mirror and in the clear and shining surface you will always see me—so will you be able to meet with me often and tell me all your heart; and though I shall not be able to speak, I shall understand and sympathize with you, whatever may happen to you in the future." With these words the dying woman handed the mirror to her daughter.

The mind of the good mother seemed to be now at rest,

and sinking back without another word her spirit passed quietly away that day.

The bereaved father and daughter were wild with grief, and they abandoned themselves to their bitter sorrow. They felt it to be impossible to take leave of the loved woman who till now had filled their whole lives and to commit her body to the earth. But this frantic burst of grief passed, and then they took possession of their own hearts again, crushed though they were in resignation. In spite of this the daughter's life seemed to her desolate. Her love for her dead mother did not grow less with time, and so keen was her remembrance, that everything in daily life, even the falling of the rain and the blowing of the wind, reminded her of her mother's death and of all that they had loved and shared together. One day when her father was out, and she was fulfilling her household duties alone, her loneliness and sorrow seemed more than she could bear. She threw herself down in her mother's room and wept as if her heart would break. Poor child, she longed just for one glimpse of the loved face, one sound of the voice calling her pet name, or for one moment's forgetfulness of the aching void in her heart. Suddenly she sat up. Her mother's last words had rung through her memory hitherto dulled by grief.

"Oh! my mother told me when she gave me the mirror as a parting gift, that whenever I looked into it I should be able to meet her—to see her. I had nearly forgotten her last words—how stupid I am; I will get the mirror now and see if it can possibly be true!"

She dried her eyes quickly, and going to the cupboard took out the box that contained the mirror, her heart beating with expectation as she lifted the mirror out and gazed into its smooth face. Behold, her mother's words were true! In the round mirror before her she saw her mother's face; but, oh, the joyful surprise! It was not her mother thin and wasted by illness, but the young and beautiful woman as she remembered her far back in the days of her own earliest childhood. It seemed to the girl that the face in the mirror must soon speak, almost that she heard the voice of her mother telling her again to grow up a good woman and a dutiful daughter, so earnestly did the eyes in the mirror look back into her own.

"It is certainly my mother's soul that I see. She knows how miserable I am without her and she has come to comfort me. Whenever I long to see her she will meet me here; how grateful I ought to be!"

And from this time the weight of sorrow was greatly lightened for her young heart. Every morning, to gather strength for the day's duties before her, and every evening, for consolation before she lay down to rest, did the young girl take out the mirror and gaze at the reflection which in the simplicity of her innocent heart she believed to be her mother's soul. Daily she grew in the likeness of her dead mother's character, and was gentle and kind to all, and a dutiful daughter to her father.

A year spent in mourning had thus passed away in the little household, when, by the advice of his relations, the man married again, and the daughter now found herself under the authority of a step-mother. It was a trying position; but her days spent in the recollection of her own beloved mother, and of trying to be what that mother would wish her to be, had made the young girl docile and patient, and she now determined to be filial and dutiful to her father's wife, in all respects. Everything went on apparently smoothly in the family for some time under the new regime; there were no winds or waves of discord to ruffle the surface of every-day life, and the father was content.

But it is a woman's danger to be petty and mean, and step-mothers are proverbial all the world over, and this one's heart was not as her first smiles were. As the days and weeks grew into months, the step-mother began to treat the motherless girl unkindly and to try and come between the father and child.

Sometimes she went to her husband and complained of her step-daughter's behavior, but the father knowing that this was to be expected, took no notice of her ill-natured complaints. Instead of lessening his affection for his daughter, as the woman desired, her grumblings only made him think of her the more. The woman soon saw that he began to show more concern for his lonely child than before. This did not please her at all, and she began to turn over in her mind how she could, by some means or other, drive her step-child out of the house. So crooked did the woman's heart become.

She watched the girl carefully, and one day peeping into her room in the early morning, she thought she discovered a grave enough sin of which to accuse the child to her father. The woman herself was a little frightened too at what she had seen.

So she went at once to her husband, and wiping away some false tears she said in a sad voice:

"Please give me permission to leave you today."

The man was completely taken by surprise at the suddenness of her request, and wondered whatever was the matter.

"Do you find it so disagreeable," he asked, "in my house, that you can stay no longer?"

"No! no! it has nothing to do with you—even in my

dreams I have never thought that I wished to leave your side; but if I go on living here I am in danger of losing my life, so I think it best for all concerned that you should allow me to go home!"

And the woman began to weep afresh. Her husband, distressed to see her so unhappy, and thinking that he could not have heard aright, said:

"Tell me what you mean! How is your life in danger here?"

"I will tell you since you ask me. Your daughter dislikes me as her step-mother. For some time past she has shut herself up in her room morning and evening, and looking in as I pass by, I am convinced that she has made an image of me and is trying to kill me by magic art, cursing me daily. It is not safe for me to stay here, such being the case; indeed, indeed, I must go away, we cannot live under the same roof any more."

The husband listened to the dreadful tale, but he could not believe his gentle daughter guilty of such an evil act. He knew that by popular superstition people believed that one person could cause the gradual death of another by making an image of the hated one and cursing it daily; but where had his young daughter learned such knowledge? The thing was impossible. Yet he remembered having noticed that his daughter stayed much in her room of late and kept herself away from every one, even when visitors came to the house. Putting this fact together with his wife's alarm, he thought that there might be something to account for the strange story.

His heart was torn between doubting his wife and trusting his child, and he knew not what to do. He decided to go at once to his daughter and try to find out the truth. Comforting his wife and assuring her that her fears were groundless, he glided quietly to his daughter's room.

The girl had for a long time past been very unhappy. She had tried by amiability and obedience to show her good-will and to mollify the new wife, and to break down that wall of prejudice and misunderstanding that she knew generally stood between step-parents and their step-children. But she soon found that her efforts were in vain. The step-mother never trusted her, and seemed to misinterpret all her actions, and the poor child knew very well that she often carried unkind and untrue tales to her father. She could not help comparing her present unhappy condition with the time when her own mother was alive only a little more than a year ago—so great a change in this short time! Morning and evening she wept over the remembrance. Whenever she could she went to her room, and sliding the screens to, took out the mirror and gazed, as she thought, at her mother's face. It was the only comfort that she had in these wretched days.

Her father found her occupied in this way. Pushing aside the fusama, he saw her bending over something or other very intently. Looking over her shoulder, to see who was entering her room, the girl was surprised to see her father, for he generally sent for her when he wished to speak to her. She was also confused at being found looking at the mirror, for she had never told any one of her mother's last promise, but had kept it as the sacred secret of her heart. So before turning to her father she slipped the mirror into her long sleeve. Her father noting her confusion, and her act of hiding something, said in a severe manner:

"Daughter, what are you doing here? And what is that that you have hidden in your sleeve?"

The girl was frightened by her father's severity. Never

had he spoken to her in such a tone. Her confusion changed to apprehension, her color from scarlet to white. She sat dumb and shamefaced, unable to reply.

Appearances were certainly against her; the young girl looked guilty, and the father thinking that perhaps after all what his wife had told him was true, spoke angrily:

"Then, is it really true that you are daily cursing your step-mother and praying for her death? Have you forgotten what I told you, that although she is your step-mother you must be obedient and loyal to her? What evil spirit has taken possession of your heart that you should be so wicked? You have certainly changed, my daughter! What has made you so disobedient and unfaithful?"

And the father's eyes filled with sudden tears to think that he should have to upbraid his daughter in this way.

She on her part did not know what he meant, for she had never heard of the superstition that by praying over an image it is possible to cause the death of a hated person. But she saw that she must speak and clear herself somehow. She loved her father dearly, and could not bear the idea of his anger. She put out her hand on his knee deprecatingly:

"Father! father! do not say such dreadful things to me. I am still your obedient child. Indeed, I am. However stupid I may be, I should never be able to curse any one who belonged to you, much less pray for the death of one you love. Surely some one has been telling you lies, and you are dazed, and you know not what you say—or some evil spirit has taken possession of YOUR heart. As for me I do not know—no, not so much as a dew-drop, of the evil thing of which you accuse me."

But the father remembered that she had hidden something away when he first entered the room, and even this

THE MIRROR OF MATSUYAMA

earnest protest did not satisfy him. He wished to clear up his doubts once for all.

"Then why are you always alone in your room these days? And tell me what is that that you have hidden in your sleeve—show it to me at once."

Then the daughter, though shy of confessing how she had cherished her mother's memory, saw that she must tell her father all in order to clear herself. So she slipped the mirror out from her long sleeve and laid it before him.

"This," she said, "is what you saw me looking at just now."

"Why," he said in great surprise, "this is the mirror that I brought as a gift to your mother when I went up to the capital many years ago! And so you have kept it all this time? Now, why do you spend so much of your time before this mirror?"

Then she told him of her mother's last words, and of how she had promised to meet her child whenever she looked into the glass. But still the father could not understand the simplicity of his daughter's character in not knowing that what she saw reflected in the mirror was in reality her own face, and not that of her mother.

"What do you mean?" he asked. "I do not understand how you can meet the soul of your lost mother by looking in this mirror?"

"It is indeed true," said the girl: "and if you don't believe what I say, look for yourself," and she placed the mirror before her. There, looking back from the smooth metal disk, was her own sweet face. She pointed to the reflection seriously:

"Do you doubt me still?" she asked earnestly, looking up into his face.

With an exclamation of sudden understanding the father

smote his two hands together.

"How stupid I am! At last I understand. Your face is as like your mother's as the two sides of a melon—thus you have looked at the reflection of your face all this time, thinking that you were brought face to face with your lost mother! You are truly a faithful child. It seems at first a stupid thing to have done, but it is not really so, It shows how deep has been your filial piety, and how innocent your heart. Living in constant remembrance of your lost mother has helped you to grow like her in character. How clever it was of her to tell you to do this. I admire and respect you, my daughter, and I am ashamed to think that for one instant I believed your suspicious step-mother's story and suspected you of evil, and came with the intention of scolding you severely, while all this time you have been so true and good. Before you I have no countenance left, and I beg you to forgive me."

And here the father wept. He thought of how lonely the poor girl must have been, and of all that she must have suffered under her step-mother's treatment. His daughter steadfastly keeping her faith and simplicity in the midst of such adverse circumstances—bearing all her troubles with so much patience and amiability—made him compare her to the lotus which rears its blossom of dazzling beauty out of the slime and mud of the moats and ponds, fitting emblem of a heart which keeps itself unsullied while passing through the world.

The step-mother, anxious to know what would happen, had all this while been standing outside the room. She had grown interested, and had gradually pushed the sliding screen back till she could see all that went on. At this moment she suddenly entered the room, and dropping to the mats, she bowed her head over her outspread hands before her step-daughter.

"I am ashamed! I am ashamed!" she exclaimed in broken tones. "I did not know what a filial child you were. Through no fault of yours, but with a step-mother's jealous heart, I have disliked you all the time. Hating you so much myself, it was but natural that I should think you reciprocated the feeling, and thus when I saw you retire so often to your room I followed you, and when I saw you gaze daily into the mirror for long intervals, I concluded that you had found out how I disliked you, and that you were out of revenge trying to take my life by magic art. As long as I live I shall never forget the wrong I have done you in so misjudging you, and in causing your father to suspect you. From this day I throw away my old and wicked heart, and in its place I put a new one, clean and full of repentance. I shall think of you as a child that I have borne myself. I shall love and cherish you with all my heart, and thus try to make up for all the unhappiness I have caused you. Therefore, please throw into the water all that has gone before, and give me, I beg of you, some of the filial love that you have hitherto given to your own lost mother."

Thus did the unkind step-mother humble herself and ask forgiveness of the girl she had so wronged.

Such was the sweetness of the girl's disposition that she willingly forgave her step-mother, and never bore a moment's resentment or malice towards her afterwards. The father saw by his wife's face that she was truly sorry for the past, and was greatly relieved to see the terrible misunderstanding wiped out of remembrance by both the wrong-doer and the wronged.

From this time on, the three lived together as happily as fish in water. No such trouble ever darkened the home again, and the young girl gradually forgot that year of unhappiness in the tender love and care that her step-mother now bestowed on her. Her patience and goodness were rewarded at last.

THE GOBLIN OF ADACHIGAHARA

Long, long ago there was a large plain called Adachigahara, in the province of Mutsu in Japan. This place was said to be haunted by a cannibal goblin who took the form of an old woman. From time to time many travelers disappeared and were never heard of more, and the old women round the charcoal braziers in the evenings, and the girls washing the household rice at the wells in the mornings, whispered dreadful stories of how the missing folk had been lured to the goblin's cottage and devoured, for the goblin lived only on human flesh. No one dared to venture near the haunted spot after sunset, and all those who could, avoided it in the daytime, and travelers were warned of the dreaded place.

One day as the sun was setting, a priest came to the plain. He was a belated traveler, and his robe showed that he was a Buddhist pilgrim walking from shrine to shrine to pray for some blessing or to crave for forgiveness of sins. He had apparently lost his way, and as it was late he met no one who could show him the road or warn him of the haunted spot.

He had walked the whole day and was now tired and hungry, and the evenings were chilly, for it was late autumn, and he began to be very anxious to find some house where he could obtain a night's lodging. He found himself lost in the midst of the large plain, and looked about in vain for some sign of human habitation.

At last, after wandering about for some hours, he saw a clump of trees in the distance, and through the trees he caught sight of the glimmer of a single ray of light. He exclaimed with joy:

"Oh. surely that is some cottage where I can get a night's lodging!"

Keeping the light before his eyes he dragged his weary, aching feet as quickly as he could towards the spot, and soon came to a miserable-looking little cottage. As he drew near he saw that it was in a tumble-down condition, the bamboo fence was broken and weeds and grass pushed their way through the gaps. The paper screens which serve as windows and doors in Japan were full of holes, and the posts of the house were bent with age and seemed scarcely able to support the old thatched roof. The hut was open, and by the light of an old lantern an old woman sat industriously spinning.

The pilgrim called to her across the bamboo fence and said:

"O Baa San (old woman), good evening! I am a traveler! Please excuse me, but I have lost my way and do not know what to do, for I have nowhere to rest to-night. I beg you to be good enough to let me spend the night under your roof."

The old woman as soon as she heard herself spoken to stopped spinning, rose from her seat and approached the intruder.

"I am very sorry for you. You must indeed be distressed to have lost your way in such a lonely spot so late at night. Unfortunately I cannot put you up, for I have no bed to offer you, and no accommodation whatsoever for a guest in this poor place!"

"Oh, that does not matter," said the priest; "all I want is a shelter under some roof for the night, and if you will be good enough just to let me lie on the kitchen floor I shall be grateful. I am too tired to walk further to-night, so I hope you will not refuse me, otherwise I shall have to sleep out on the cold plain." And in this way he pressed the old woman to let him stay.

She seemed very reluctant, but at last she said:

"Very well, I will let you stay here. I can offer you a very poor welcome only, but come in now and I will make a fire, for the night is cold."

The pilgrim was only too glad to do as he was told. He took off his sandals and entered the hut. The old woman then brought some sticks of wood and lit the fire, and bade her guest draw near and warm himself.

"You must be hungry after your long tramp," said the old woman. "I will go and cook some supper for you." She then went to the kitchen to cook some rice.

After the priest had finished his supper the old woman sat down by the fire-place, and they talked together for a long time. The pilgrim thought to himself that he had been very lucky to come across such a kind, hospitable old woman. At last the wood gave out, and as the fire died slowly down he began to shiver with cold just as he had done when he arrived.

"I see you are cold," said the old woman; "I will go out and gather some wood, for we have used it all. You must stay and take care of the house while I am gone."

"No, no," said the pilgrim, "let me go instead, for you are old, and I cannot think of letting you go out to get wood for me this cold night!"

The old woman shook her head and said:

"You must stay quietly here, for you are my guest." Then she left him and went out.

In a minute she came back and said:

"You must sit where you are and not move, and whatever happens don't go near or look into the inner room. Now mind what I tell you!"

"If you tell me not to go near the back room, of course I won't," said the priest, rather bewildered.

The old woman then went out again, and the priest was left alone. The fire had died out, and the only light in the hut was that of a dim lantern. For the first time that night he began to feel that he was in a weird place, and the old woman's words, "Whatever you do don't peep into the back room," aroused his curiosity and his fear.

What hidden thing could be in that room that she did not wish him to see? For some time the remembrance of his promise to the old woman kept him still, but at last he could no longer resist his curiosity to peep into the forbidden place.

He got up and began to move slowly towards the back room. Then the thought that the old woman would be very angry with him if he disobeyed her made him come back to his place by the fireside.

As the minutes went slowly by and the old woman did not return, he began to feel more and more frightened, and to wonder what dreadful secret was in the room behind him. He must find out.

"She will not know that I have looked unless I tell her. I will just have a peep before she comes back," said the man to himself.

With these words he got up on his feet (for he had been sitting all this time in Japanese fashion with his feet under him) and stealthily crept towards the forbidden spot. With trembling hands he pushed back the sliding door and looked in. What he saw froze the blood in his veins. The room was full of dead men's bones and the walls were splashed and the floor was covered with human blood. In one corner skull upon skull rose to the ceiling, in another was a heap of arm bones, in another a heap of leg bones. The sickening smell made him faint. He fell backwards with horror, and for some time lay in a heap with fright on the floor, a pitiful sight. He trembled all over and his teeth chattered, and he could hardly crawl away from the dreadful spot.

"How horrible!" he cried out. "What awful den have I come to in my travels? May Buddha help me or I am lost. Is it possible that that kind old woman is really the cannibal goblin? When she comes back she will show herself in her true character and eat me up at one mouthful!"

With these words his strength came back to him and, snatching up his hat and staff, he rushed out of the house as fast as his legs could carry him. Out into the night he ran, his one thought to get as far as he could from the goblin's haunt. He had not gone far when he heard steps behind him and a voice crying: "Stop! stop!"

He ran on, redoubling his speed, pretending not to hear. As he ran he heard the steps behind him come nearer and nearer, and at last he recognized the old woman's voice which grew louder and louder as she came nearer.

"Stop! stop, you wicked man, why did you look into the forbidden room?"

The priest quite forgot how tired he was and his feet flew over the ground faster than ever. Fear gave him strength, for he knew that if the goblin caught him he would soon be one of her victims. With all his heart he repeated the prayer to Buddha:

"Namu Amida Butsu, Namu Amida Butsu."

And after him rushed the dreadful old hag, her hair flying in the wind, and her face changing with rage into the demon that she was. In her hand she carried a large blood-stained knife, and she still shrieked after him, "Stop! stop!"

At last, when the priest felt he could run no more, the dawn broke, and with the darkness of night the goblin vanished and he was safe. The priest now knew that he had met the Goblin of Adachigahara, the story of whom he had often heard but never believed to be true. He felt that he owed his wonderful escape to the protection of Buddha to whom he had prayed for help, so he took out his rosary and bowing his head as the sun rose he said his prayers and made his thanksgiving earnestly. He then set forward for another part of the country, only too glad to leave the haunted plain behind him.

THE SAGACIOUS MONKEY
AND THE BOAR

Long, long ago, there lived in the province of Shinshin in Japan, a traveling monkey-man, who earned his living by taking round a monkey and showing off the animal's tricks.

One evening the man came home in a very bad temper and told his wife to send for the butcher the next morning.

The wife was very bewildered and asked her husband:

"Why do you wish me to send for the butcher?"

"It's no use taking that monkey round any longer, he's too old and forgets his tricks. I beat him with my stick all I know how, but he won't dance properly. I must now sell him to the butcher and make what money out of him I can. There is nothing else to be done."

The woman felt very sorry for the poor little animal, and pleaded for her husband to spare the monkey, but her pleading was all in vain, the man was determined to sell him to the butcher.

Now the monkey was in the next room and overheard every word of the conversation. He soon understood that he was to be killed, and he said to himself:

"Barbarous, indeed, is my master! Here I have served him faithfully for years, and instead of allowing me to end my days comfortably and in peace, he is going to let me be cut up by the butcher, and my poor body is to be roasted and stewed and eaten? Woe is me! What am I to do. Ah! a bright thought has struck me! There is, I know, a wild bear living in the forest near by. I have often heard tell of his wisdom. Perhaps if I go to him and tell him the strait I am in he will give me his counsel. I will go and try."

There was no time to lose. The monkey slipped out of the house and ran as quickly as he could to the forest to find the boar. The boar was at home, and the monkey began his tale of woe at once.

"Good Mr. Boar, I have heard of your excellent wisdom. I am in great trouble, you alone can help me. I have grown old in the service of my master, and because I cannot dance properly now he intends to sell me to the butcher. What do you advise me to do? I know how clever you are!"

The boar was pleased at the flattery and determined to help the monkey. He thought for a little while and then said:

"Hasn't your master a baby?"

"Oh, yes," said the monkey, "he has one infant son."

"Doesn't it lie by the door in the morning when your mistress begins the work of the day? Well, I will come round early and when I see my opportunity I will seize the child and run off with it."

"What then?" said the monkey.

"Why the mother will be in a tremendous scare, and before your master and mistress know what to do, you must run after me and rescue the child and take it home safely to its parents, and you will see that when the butcher comes they won't have the heart to sell you."

The monkey thanked the boar many times and then went home. He did not sleep much that night, as you may imagine, for thinking of the morrow. His life depended on whether the boar's plan succeeded or not. He was the first up, waiting anxiously for what was to happen. It seemed to him a very long time before his master's wife began to move about and open the shutters to let in the light of day. Then all happened as the boar had planned. The mother placed her child near the porch as usual while she tidied up the house and got her breakfast ready.

The child was crooning happily in the morning sunlight, dabbing on the mats at the play of light and shadow. Suddenly there was a noise in the porch and a loud cry from the child. The mother ran out from the kitchen to the spot, only just in time to see the boar disappearing through the gate with her child in its clutch. She flung out her hands with a loud cry of despair and rushed into the inner room where her husband was still sleeping soundly.

He sat up slowly and rubbed his eyes, and crossly demanded what his wife was making all that noise about. By the time that the man was alive to what had happened, and they both got outside the gate, the boar had got well away, but they saw the monkey running after the thief as hard as his legs would carry him.

Both the man and wife were moved to admiration at the plucky conduct of the sagacious monkey, and their gratitude knew no bounds when the faithful monkey brought the child safely back to their arms.

"There!" said the wife. "This is the animal you want to kill—if the monkey hadn't been here we should have lost our child forever."

"You are right, wife, for once," said the man as he carried the child into the house. "You may send the butcher back when he comes, and now give us all a good breakfast and the monkey too."

When the butcher arrived he was sent away with an order for some boar's meat for the evening dinner, and the monkey was petted and lived the rest of his days in peace, nor did his master ever strike him again.

THE HAPPY HUNTER AND
THE SKILLFUL FISHER

Long, long ago Japan was governed by Hohodemi, the fourth Mikoto (or Augustness) in descent from the illustrious Amaterasu, the Sun Goddess. He was not only as handsome as his ancestress was beautiful, but he was also very strong and brave, and was famous for being the greatest hunter in the land. Because of his matchless skill as a hunter, he was called "Yama-sachi-hiko" or "The Happy Hunter of the Mountains."

His elder brother was a very skillful fisher, and as he far surpassed all rivals in fishing, he was named "Umi-sachi-hiko" or the "Skillful Fisher of the Sea." The brothers thus led happy lives, thoroughly enjoying their respective occupations, and the days passed quickly and pleasantly while each pursued his own way, the one hunting and the other fishing.

One day the Happy Hunter came to his brother, the Skillful Fisher, and said:

"Well, my brother, I see you go to the sea every day with your fishing rod in your hand, and when you return you come laden with fish. And as for me, it is my pleasure to take my bow and arrow and to hunt the wild animals up the mountains and down in the valleys. For a long time we have each followed our favorite occupation, so that now we must both be tired, you of your fishing and I of my hunting. Would it not be wise for us to make a change? Will you try hunting in the mountains and I will go and fish in the sea?"

The Skillful Fisher listened in silence to his brother, and for a moment was thoughtful, but at last he answered:

"O yes, why not? Your idea is not a bad one at all. Give me your bow and arrow and I will set out at once for the mountains and hunt for game."

So the matter was settled by this talk, and the two brothers each started out to try the other's occupation, little dreaming of all that would happen. It was very unwise of them, for the Happy Hunter knew nothing of fishing, and the Skillful Fisher, who was bad tempered, knew as much about hunting.

The Happy Hunter took his brother's much-prized fishing hook and rod and went down to the seashore and sat down on the rocks. He baited his hook and then threw it into the sea clumsily. He sat and gazed at the little float bobbing up and down in the water, and longed for a good fish to come and be caught. Every time the buoy moved a little he pulled up his rod, but there was never a fish at the end of it, only the hook and the bait. If he had known how to fish properly, he would have been able to catch plenty of fish, but although he was the greatest hunter in the land he could not help being the most bungling fisher.

The whole day passed in this way, while he sat on the rocks holding the fishing rod and waiting in vain for his luck to turn. At last the day began to darken, and the evening came; still he had caught not a single fish. Drawing up his line for the last time before going home, he found that he had lost his hook without even knowing when he had dropped it.

He now began to feel extremely anxious, for he knew that his brother would be angry at his having lost his hook, for, it being his only one, he valued it above all other things. The Happy Hunter now set to work to look among the rocks and on the sand for the lost hook, and while he was searching to and fro, his brother, the Skillful Fisher, arrived on the scene. He had failed to find any game while hunting that day, and was not only in a bad temper, but looked fearfully cross.

When he saw the Happy Hunter searching about on the shore he knew that something must have gone wrong, so he said at once:

"What are you doing, my brother?"

The Happy Hunter went forward timidly, for he feared his brother's anger, and said:

"Oh, my brother, I have indeed done badly."

"What is the matter? What have you done?" asked the elder brother impatiently.

"I have lost your precious fishing hook—"

While he was still speaking his brother stopped him, and cried out fiercely:

"Lost my hook! It is just what I expected. For this reason, when you first proposed your plan of changing over our occupations I was really against it, but you seemed to wish it so much that I gave in and allowed you to do as you wished. The mistake of our trying unfamiliar tasks is soon seen! And you have done badly. I will not return you your bow and arrow till you have found my hook. Look to it that you find it and return it to me quickly."

The Happy Hunter felt that he was to blame for all that had come to pass, and bore his brother's scornful scolding with humility and patience. He hunted everywhere for the hook most diligently, but it was nowhere to be found. He was at last obliged to give up all hope of finding it. He then went home, and in desperation broke his beloved sword into pieces and made five hundred hooks out of it.

He took these to his angry brother and offered them to him, asking his forgiveness, and begging him to accept them in the place of the one he had lost for him. It was useless; his brother would not listen to him, much less grant his request.

The Happy Hunter then made another five hundred hooks, and again took them to his brother, beseeching him to pardon him.

"Though you make a million hooks," said the Skillful Fisher, shaking his head, "they are of no use to me. I cannot forgive you unless you bring me back my own hook."

Nothing would appease the anger of the Skillful Fisher, for he had a bad disposition, and had always hated his brother because of his virtues, and now with the excuse of the lost fishing hook he planned to kill him and to usurp his place as ruler of Japan. The Happy Hunter knew all this full well, but he could say nothing, for being the younger he owed his elder brother obedience; so he returned to the seashore and once more began to look for the missing hook. He was much cast down, for he had lost all hope of ever finding his brother's hook now. While he stood on the beach, lost in perplexity and wondering what he had best do next, an old man suddenly appeared carrying a stick in his hand. The Happy Hunter afterwards remembered that he did not see from whence the old man came, neither did he know how he was there—he happened to look up and saw the old man coming towards him.

"You are Hohodemi, the Augustness, sometimes called the Happy Hunter, are you not?" asked the old man. "What are you doing alone in such a place?"

"Yes, I am he," answered the unhappy young man. "Unfortunately, while fishing I lost my brother's precious fishing hook. I have hunted this shore all over, but alas! I cannot find it, and I am very troubled, for my brother won't forgive me till I restore it to him. But who are you?"

"My name is Shiwozuchino Okina, and I live near by on this shore. I am sorry to hear what misfortune has befallen you. You must indeed be anxious. But if I tell you what I think, the hook is nowhere here—it is either at the bottom of the sea or in the body of some fish who has swallowed it, and for this reason, though you spend your whole life in looking for it here, you will never find it."

"Then what can I do?" asked the distressed man.

"You had better go down to Ryn Gu and tell Ryn Jin, the Dragon King of the Sea, what your trouble is and ask him to find the hook for you. I think that would be the best way."

"Your idea is a splendid one," said the Happy Hunter, "but I fear I cannot get to the Sea King's realm, for I have always heard that it is situated at the bottom of the sea."

"Oh, there will be no difficulty about your getting there," said the old man; "I can soon make something for you to ride on through the sea."

"Thank you," said the Happy Hunter, "I shall be very grateful to you if you will be so kind."

The old man at once set to work, and soon made a basket and offered it to the Happy Hunter. He received it with joy, and taking it to the water, mounted it, and prepared to start. He bade good by to the kind old man who had helped him so much, and told him that he would certainly reward him as soon as he found his hook and could return to Japan without fear of his brother's anger. The old man pointed out the direction he must take, and told him how to reach the realm of Ryn Gu, and watched him ride out to sea on the basket, which resembled a small boat.

The Happy Hunter made all the haste he could, riding on the basket which had been given him by his friend. His queer boat seemed to go through the water of its own accord, and the distance was much shorter than he had expected, for in a few hours he caught sight of the gate and the roof of the Sea King's Palace. And what a large place it was, with its numberless sloping roofs and gables, its huge gateways, and its gray stone walls! He soon landed, and leaving his basket on the beach, he walked up to the large gateway. The pillars of the gate were made of beautiful red coral, and the gate itself was adorned with glittering gems of all kinds. Large katsura trees overshadowed it. Our hero had often heard of the wonders of the Sea King's Palace beneath the sea, but all the stories he had ever heard fell short of the reality which he now saw for the first time.

The Happy Hunter would have liked to enter the gate there and then, but he saw that it was fast closed, and also that there was no one about whom he could ask to open it for him, so he stopped to think what he should do. In the shade of the trees before the gate he noticed a well full of fresh spring water. Surely some one would come out to draw water from the well some time, he thought. Then he climbed into the tree overhanging the well, and seated himself to rest on one of the branches, and waited for what might happen. Ere long he saw the huge gate swing open, and two beautiful women came out. Now the Mikoto (Augustness) had always heard that Ryn Gu was the realm of the Dragon King under the Sea, and had naturally supposed that the place was inhabited by dragons and similar terrible creatures, so that when he saw these two lovely princesses, whose beauty would be rare even in the world from which he had just come, he was exceedingly surprised, and wondered what it could mean.

He said not a word, however, but silently gazed at them through the foliage of the trees, waiting to see what they would do. He saw that in their hands they carried golden buckets.

Slowly and gracefully in their trailing garments they approached the well, standing in the shade of the katsura trees, and were about to draw water, all unknowing of the stranger who was watching them, for the Happy Hunter was quite hidden among the branches of the tree where he had posted himself.

As the two ladies leaned over the side of the well to let down their golden buckets, which they did every day in the year, they saw reflected in the deep still water the face of a handsome youth gazing at them from amidst the branches of the tree in whose shade they stood. Never before had they seen the face of mortal man; they were frightened, and drew back quickly with their golden buckets in their hands. Their curiosity, however, soon gave them courage, and they glanced timidly upwards to see the cause of the unusual reflection, and then they beheld the Happy Hunter sitting in the tree looking down at them with surprise and admiration. They gazed at him face to face, but their tongues were still with wonder and could not find a word to say to him.

When the Mikoto saw that he was discovered, he sprang down lightly from the tree and said:

"I am a traveler, and as I was very thirsty I came to the well in the hopes of quenching my thirst, but I could find no bucket with which to draw the water. So I climbed into the tree, much vexed, and waited for some one to come. Just at that moment, while I was thirstily and impatiently waiting, you noble ladies appeared, as if in answer to my great need. Therefore I pray you of your mercy give me some water to drink, for I am a thirsty traveler in a strange land."

His dignity and graciousness overruled their timidity, and bowing in silence they both once more approached the well, and letting down their golden buckets drew up some water and poured it into a jeweled cup and offered it to the stranger.

He received it from them with both hands, raising it to the height of his forehead in token of high respect and pleasure, and then drank the water quickly, for his thirst was great. When he had finished his long draught he set the cup down on the edge of the well, and drawing his short sword he cut off one of the strange curved jewels (magatama), a necklace of which hung round his neck and fell over his breast. He placed the jewel in the cup and returned it to them, and said, bowing deeply:

"This is a token of my thanks!"

The two ladies took the cup, and looking into it to see what he had put inside—for they did not yet know what it was—they gave a start of surprise, for there lay a beautiful gem at the bottom of the cup.

"No ordinary mortal would give away a jewel so freely. Will you not honor us by telling us who you are?" said the elder damsel.

"Certainly," said the Happy Hunter, "I am Hohodemi, the fourth Mikoto, also called in Japan, the Happy Hunter."

"Are you indeed Hohodemi, the grandson of Amaterasu, the Sun Goddess?" asked the damsel who had spoken first. "I am the eldest daughter of Ryn Jin, the King of the Sea, and my name is Princess Tayotama."

"And," said the younger maiden, who at last found her tongue, "I am her sister, the Princess Tamayori."

"Are you indeed the daughters of Ryn Jin, the King of the Sea? I cannot tell you how glad I am to meet you," said the Happy Hunter. And without waiting for them to reply he went on:

"The other day I went fishing with my brother's hook and dropped it, how, I am sure I can't tell. As my brother prizes his fishing hook above all his other possessions, this is the greatest calamity that could have befallen me. Unless I find it again I can never hope to win my brother's forgiveness, for he is very angry at what I have done. I have searched for it many, many times, but I cannot find it, therefore I am much troubled. While I was hunting for the hook, in great distress, I met a wise old man, and he told me that the best thing I could do was to come to Ryn Gu, and to Ryn Jin, the Dragon King of the Sea, and ask him to help me. This kind old man also showed me how to come. Now you know how it is I am here and why. I want to ask Ryn Jin, if he knows where the lost hook is. Will you be so kind as to take me to your father? And do you think he will see me?" asked the Happy Hunter anxiously.

Princess Tayotama listened to this long story, and then said:

"Not only is it easy for you to see my father, but he will be much pleased to meet you. I am sure he will say that good fortune has befallen him, that so great and noble a man as you, the grandson of Amaterasu, should come down to the bottom of the sea." And then turning to her younger sister, she said:

"Do you not think so, Tamayori?"

"Yes, indeed," answered the Princess Tamayori, in her sweet voice. "As you say, we can know no greater honor than to welcome the Mikoto to our home."

"Then I ask you to be so kind as to lead the way," said the Happy Hunter.

"Condescend to enter, Mikoto (Augustness)," said both the sisters, and bowing low, they led him through the gate.

The younger Princess left her sister to take charge of the Happy Hunter, and going faster than they, she reached the Sea King's Palace first, and running quickly to her father's room, she told him of all that had happened to them at the gate, and that her sister was even now bringing the Augustness to him. The Dragon King of the Sea was much surprised at the news, for it was but seldom, perhaps only once in several hundred years, that the Sea King's Palace was visited by mortals.

Ryn Jin at once clapped his hands and summoned all his courtiers and the servants of the Palace, and the chief fish of the sea together, and solemnly told them that the grandson of the Sun Goddess, Amaterasu, was coming to the Palace, and that they must be very ceremonious and polite in serving the august visitor. He then ordered them all to the entrance of the Palace to welcome the Happy Hunter.

Ryn Jin then dressed himself in his robes of ceremony, and went out to welcome him. In a few moments the Princess Tayotama and the Happy Hunter reached the entrance, and the Sea King and his wife bowed to the ground and thanked him for the honor he did them in coming to see them. The Sea King then led the Happy Hunter to the guest room, and placing him in the uppermost seat, he bowed respectfully before him, and said:

"I am Ryn Jin, the Dragon King of the Sea, and this is my wife. Condescend to remember us forever!"

"Are you indeed Ryn Jin, the King of the Sea, of whom I have so often heard?" answered the Happy Hunter, saluting his host most ceremoniously. "I must apologize for all the trouble I am giving you by my unexpected visit." And he bowed again, and thanked the Sea King.

"You need not thank me," said Ryn Jin. "It is I who must

thank you for coming. Although the Sea Palace is a poor place, as you see, I shall be highly honored if you will make us a long visit."

There was much gladness between the Sea King and the Happy Hunter, and they sat and talked for a long time. At last the Sea King clapped his hands, and then a huge retinue of fishes appeared, all robed in ceremonial garments, and bearing in their fins various trays on which all kinds of sea delicacies were served. A great feast was now spread before the King and his Royal guest. All the fishes-in-waiting were chosen from amongst the finest fish in the sea, so you can imagine what a wonderful array of sea creatures it was that waited upon the Happy Hunter that day. All in the Palace tried to do their best to please him and to show him that he was a much honored guest. During the long repast, which lasted for hours, Ryn Jin commanded his daughters to play some music, and the two Princesses came in and performed on the KOTO (the Japanese harp), and sang and danced in turns. The time passed so pleasantly that the Happy Hunter seemed to forget his trouble and why he had come at all to the Sea King's Realm, and he gave himself up to the enjoyment of this wonderful place, the land of fairy fishes! Who has ever heard of such a marvelous place? But the Mikoto soon remembered what had brought him to Ryn Gu, and said to his host:

"Perhaps your daughters have told you, King Ryn Jin, that I have come here to try and recover my brother's fishing hook, which I lost while fishing the other day. May I ask you to be so kind as to inquire of all your subjects if any of them have seen a fishing hook lost in the sea?"

"Certainly," said the obliging Sea King, "I will immediately summon them all here and ask them."

As soon as he had issued his command, the octopus, the cuttlefish, the bonito, the oxtail fish, the eel, the jelly fish, the shrimp, and the plaice, and many other fishes of all kinds came in and sat down before Ryn Jin their King, and arranged themselves and their fins in order. Then the Sea King said solemnly:

"Our visitor who is sitting before you all is the august grandson of Amaterasu. His name is Hohodemi, the fourth Augustness, and he is also called the Happy Hunter of the Mountains. While he was fishing the other day upon the shore of Japan, some one robbed him of his brother's fishing hook. He has come all this way down to the bottom of the sea to our Kingdom because he thought that one of you fishes may have taken the hook from him in mischievous play. If any of you have done so you must immediately return it, or if any of you know who the thief is you must at once tell us his name and where he is now."

All the fishes were taken by surprise when they heard these words, and could say nothing for some time. They sat looking at each other and at the Dragon King. At last the cuttlefish came forward and said:

"I think the TAI (the red bream) must be the thief who has stolen the hook!"

"Where is your proof?" asked the King.

"Since yesterday evening the TAI has not been able to eat anything, and he seems to be suffering from a bad throat! For this reason I think the hook may be in his throat. You had better send for him at once!"

All the fish agreed to this, and said:

"It is certainly strange that the TAI is the only fish who has not obeyed your summons. Will you send for him and inquire into the matter. Then our innocence will be proved."

"Yes," said the Sea King, "it is strange that the TAI has not come, for he ought to be the first to be here. Send for him at once!"

Without waiting for the King's order the cuttlefish had already started for the TAI'S dwelling, and he now returned, bringing the TAI with him. He led him before the King.

The TAI sat there looking frightened and ill. He certainly was in pain, for his usually red face was pale, and his eyes were nearly closed and looked but half their usual size.

"Answer, O TAI!" cried the Sea King, "why did you not come in answer to my summons today?"

"I have been ill since yesterday," answered the TAI; "that is why I could not come."

"Don't say another word!" cried out Ryn Jin angrily. "Your illness is the punishment of the gods for stealing the Mikoto's hook."

"It is only too true!" said the TAI; "the hook is still in my throat, and all my efforts to get it out have been useless. I can't eat, and I can scarcely breathe, and each moment I feel that it will choke me, and sometimes it gives me great pain. I had no intention of stealing the Mikoto's hook. I heedlessly snapped at the bait which I saw in the water, and the hook came off and stuck in my throat. So I hope you will pardon me."

The cuttlefish now came forward, and said to the King:

"What I said was right. You see the hook still sticks in the TAI'S throat. I hope to be able to pull it out in the presence of the Mikoto, and then we can return it to him safely!"

"O please make haste and pull it out!" cried the TAI, pitifully, for he felt the pains in his throat coming on again; "I do so want to return the hook to the Mikoto."

"All right, TAI SAN," said his friend the cuttlefish, and then opening the TAI'S mouth as wide as he could and putting one of his feelers down the TAI'S throat, he quickly and easily drew the hook out of the sufferer's large mouth. He then washed it and brought it to the King.

Ryn Jin took the hook from his subject, and then respectfully returned it to the Happy Hunter (the Mikoto or Augustness, the fishes called him), who was overjoyed at getting back his hook. He thanked Ryn Jin many times, his face beaming with gratitude, and said that he owed the happy ending of his quest to the Sea King's wise authority and kindness.

Ryn Jin now desired to punish the TAI, but the Happy Hunter begged him not to do so; since his lost hook was thus happily recovered he did not wish to make more trouble for the poor TAI. It was indeed the TAI who had taken the hook, but he had already suffered enough for his fault, if fault it could be called. What had been done was done in heedlessness and not by intention. The Happy Hunter said he blamed himself; if he had understood how to fish properly he would never have lost his hook, and therefore all this trouble had been caused in the first place by his trying to do something which he did not know how to do. So he begged the Sea King to forgive his subject.

Who could resist the pleading of so wise and compassionate a judge? Ryn Jin forgave his subject at once at the request of his august guest. The TAI was so glad that he shook his fins for joy, and he and all the other fish went out from the presence of their King, praising the virtues of the Happy Hunter.

Now that the hook was found the Happy Hunter had nothing to keep him in Ryn Gu, and he was anxious to get back to his own kingdom and to make peace with his angry brother, the Skillful Fisher; but the Sea King, who had learnt to love him and would fain have kept him as a son, begged him not to go so soon, but to make the Sea Palace his home as long as ever he liked. While the Happy Hunter was still hesitating, the two lovely Princesses, Tayotama and Tamayori, came, and with the sweetest of bows and voices joined with their father in pressing him to stay, so that without seeming ungracious he could not say them "Nay," and was obliged to stay on for some time.

Between the Sea Realm and the Earth there was no difference in the night of time, and the Happy Hunter found that three years went fleeting quickly by in this delightful land. The years pass swiftly when any one is truly happy. But though the wonders of that enchanted land seemed to be new every day, and though the Sea King's kindness seemed rather to increase than to grow less with time, the Happy Hunter grew more and more homesick as the days passed, and he could not repress a great anxiety to know what had happened to his home and his country and his brother while he had been away.

So at last he went to the Sea King and said:

"My stay with you here has been most happy and I am very grateful to you for all your kindness to me, but I govern Japan, and, delightful as this place is, I cannot absent myself forever from my country. I must also return the fishing hook to my brother and ask his forgiveness for having deprived him of it for so long. I am indeed very sorry to part from you, but this time it cannot be helped. With your gracious permission, I will take my leave to-day. I hope to make you another visit some day. Please give up the idea of my staying longer now."

King Ryn Jin was overcome with sorrow at the thought

that he must lose his friend who had made a great diversion in the Palace of the Sea, and his tears fell fast as he answered:

"We are indeed very sorry to part with you, Mikoto, for we have enjoyed your stay with us very much. You have been a noble and honored guest and we have heartily made you welcome. I quite understand that as you govern Japan you ought to be there and not here, and that it is vain for us to try and keep you longer with us, much as we would like to have you stay. I hope you will not forget us. Strange circumstances have brought us together and I trust the friendship thus begun between the Land and the Sea will last and grow stronger than it has ever been before."

When the Sea King had finished speaking he turned to his two daughters and bade them bring him the two Tide-Jewels of the Sea. The two Princesses bowed low, rose and glided out of the hall. In a few minutes they returned, each one carrying in her hands a flashing gem which filled the room with light. As the Happy Hunter looked at them he wondered what they could be. The Sea King took them from his daughters and said to his guest:

"These two valuable talismans we have inherited from our ancestors from time immemorial. We now give them to you as a parting gift in token of our great affection for you. These two gems are called the nanjiu and the kanjiu."

The Happy Hunter bowed low to the ground and said:

"I can never thank you enough for all your kindness to me. And now will you add one more favor to the rest and tell me what these jewels are and what I am to do with them?"

"The nanjiu," answered the Sea King, "is also called the Jewel of the Flood Tide, and whoever holds it in his possession can command the sea to roll in and to flood the land at any time that he wills. The kanjiu is also called the Jewel of the Ebbing Tide, and this gem controls the sea and the waves thereof, and will cause even a tidal wave to recede."

Then Ryn Jin showed his friend how to use the talismans one by one and handed them to him. The Happy Hunter was very glad to have these two wonderful gems, the Jewel of the Flood Tide and the Jewel of the Ebbing Tide, to take back with him, for he felt that they would preserve him in case of danger from enemies at any time. After thanking his kind host again and again, he prepared to depart. The Sea King and the two Princesses, Tayotama and Tamayori, and all the inmates of the Palace, came out to say "Good-by," and before the sound of the last farewell had died away the Happy Hunter passed out from under the gateway, past the well of happy memory standing in the shade of the great KATSURA trees on his way to the beach.

Here he found, instead of the queer basket on which he had come to the Realm of Ryn Gu, a large crocodile waiting for him. Never had he seen such a huge creature. It measured eight fathoms in length from the tip of its tail to the end of its long mouth. The Sea King had ordered the monster to carry the Happy Hunter back to Japan. Like the wonderful basket which Shiwozuchino Okina had made, it could travel faster than any steamboat, and in this strange way, riding on the back of a crocodile, the Happy Hunter returned to his own land.

As soon as the crocodile landed him, the Happy Hunter hastened to tell the Skillful Fisher of his safe return. He then gave him back the fishing hook which had been found in the mouth of the TAI and which had been the cause of so much trouble between them. He earnestly begged his brother's forgiveness, telling him all that had happened to him in the Sea King's Palace and what wonderful adventures had led to the finding of the hook.

Now the Skillful Fisher had used the lost hook as an excuse for driving his brother out of the country. When his brother had left him that day three years ago, and had not returned, he had been very glad in his evil heart and had at once usurped his brother's place as ruler of the land, and had become powerful and rich. Now in the midst of enjoying what did not belong to him, and hoping that his brother might never return to claim his rights, quite unexpectedly there stood the Happy Hunter before him.

The Skillful Fisher feigned forgiveness, for he could make no more excuses for sending his brother away again, but in his heart he was very angry and hated his brother more and more, till at last he could no longer bear the sight of him day after day, and planned and watched for an opportunity to kill him.

One day when the Happy Hunter was walking in the rice fields his brother followed him with a dagger. The Happy Hunter knew that his brother was following him to kill him, and he felt that now, in this hour of great danger, was the time to use the Jewels of the Flow and Ebb of the Tide and prove whether what the Sea King had told him was true or not.

So he took out the Jewel of the Flood Tide from the bosom of his dress and raised it to his forehead. Instantly over the fields and over the farms the sea came rolling in wave upon wave till it reached the spot where his brother was standing. The Skillful Fisher stood amazed and terrified to see what was happening. In another minute he was struggling in the water and calling on his brother to save him from drowning.

The Happy Hunter had a kind heart and could not bear

the sight of his brother's distress. He at once put back the Jewel of the Flood Tide and took out the Jewel of the Ebb Tide. No sooner did he hold it up as high as his forehead than the sea ran back and back, and ere long the tossing rolling floods had vanished, and the farms and fields and dry land appeared as before.

The Skillful Fisher was very frightened at the peril of death in which he had stood, and was greatly impressed by the wonderful things he had seen his brother do. He learned now that he was making a fatal mistake to set himself against his brother, younger than he thought he was, for he now had become so powerful that the sea would flow in and the tide ebb at his word of command. So he humbled himself before the Happy Hunter and asked him to forgive him all the wrong he had done him. The Skillful Fisher promised to restore his brother to his rights and also swore that though the Happy Hunter was the younger brother and owed him allegiance by right of birth, that he, the Skillful Fisher, would exalt him as his superior and bow before him as Lord of all Japan.

Then the Happy Hunter said that he would forgive his brother if he would throw into the receding tide all his evil ways. The Skillful Fisher promised and there was peace between the two brothers. From this time he kept his word and became a good man and a kind brother.

The Happy Hunter now ruled his Kingdom without being disturbed by family strife, and there was peace in Japan for a long, long time. Above all the treasures in his house he prized the wonderful Jewels of the Flow and Ebb of the Tide which had been given him by Ryn Jin, the Dragon King of the Sea.

This is the congratulatory ending of the Happy Hunter

and the Skillful Fisher.

THE STORY OF THE OLD MAN WHO MADE WITHERED TREES TO FLOWER

Long, long ago there lived an old man and his wife who supported themselves by cultivating a small plot of land. Their life had been a very happy and peaceful one save for one great sorrow, and this was they had no child. Their only pet was a dog named Shiro, and on him they lavished all the affection of their old age. Indeed, they loved him so much that whenever they had anything nice to eat they denied themselves to give it to Shiro. Now Shiro means "white," and he was so called because of his color. He was a real Japanese dog, and very like a small wolf in appearance.

The happiest hour of the day both for the old man and his dog was when the man returned from his work in the field, and having finished his frugal supper of rice and vegetables, would take what he had saved from the meal out to the little veranda that ran round the cottage. Sure enough, Shiro was waiting for his master and the evening tit-bit. Then the old man said "Chin, chin!" and Shiro sat up and begged, and his master gave him the food. Next door to this good old couple there lived another old man and his wife who were both wicked and cruel, and who hated their good neighbors and the dog Shiro with all their might. Whenever Shiro happened to look into their kitchen they at once kicked him or threw something at him, sometimes even wounding him.

One day Shiro was heard barking for a long time in the field at the back of his master's house. The old man, thinking that perhaps some birds were attacking the corn, hurried out to see what was the matter. As soon as Shiro saw his master he ran to meet him, wagging his tail, and, seizing the end of his kimono, dragged him under a large yenoki tree. Here he began to dig very industriously with his paws, yelping with joy all the time. The old man, unable to understand what it all meant, stood looking on in bewilderment. But Shiro went on barking and digging with all his might.

The thought that something might be hidden beneath the tree, and that the dog had scented it, at last struck the old man. He ran back to the house, fetched his spade and began to dig the ground at that spot. What was his astonishment when, after digging for some time, he came upon a heap of old and valuable coins, and the deeper he dug the more gold coins did he find. So intent was the old man on his work that he never saw the cross face of his neighbor peering at him through the bamboo hedge. At last all the gold coins lay shining on the ground. Shiro sat by erect with pride and looking fondly at his master as if to say, "You see, though only a dog, I can make some return for all the kindness you show me."

The old man ran in to call his wife, and together they carried home the treasure. Thus in one day the poor old man became rich. His gratitude to the faithful dog knew no bounds, and he loved and petted him more than ever, if that were possible.

The cross old neighbor, attracted by Shiro's barking, had been an unseen and envious witness of the finding of the treasure. He began to think that he, too, would like to find a fortune. So a few days later he called at the old man's house and very ceremoniously asked permission to borrow Shiro for a short time.

Shiro's master thought this a strange request, because

he knew quite well that not only did his neighbor not love his pet dog, but that he never lost an opportunity of striking and tormenting him whenever the dog crossed his path. But the good old man was too kind-hearted to refuse his neighbor, so he consented to lend the dog on condition that he should be taken great care of.

The wicked old man returned to his home with an evil smile on his face, and told his wife how he had succeeded in his crafty intentions. He then took his spade and hastened to his own field, forcing the unwilling Shiro to follow him. As soon as he reached a yenoki tree, he said to the dog, threateningly:

"If there were gold coins under your master's tree, there must also be gold coins under my tree. You must find them for me! Where are they? Where? Where?"

And catching hold of Shiro's neck he held the dog's head to the ground, so that Shiro began to scratch and dig in order to free himself from the horrid old man's grasp.

The old man was very pleased when he saw the dog begin to scratch and dig, for he at once supposed that some gold coins lay buried under his tree as well as under his neighbor's, and that the dog had scented them as before; so pushing Shiro away he began to dig himself, but there was nothing to be found. As he went on digging a foul smell was noticeable, and he at last came upon a refuse heap.

The old man's disgust can be imagined. This soon gave way to anger. He had seen his neighbor's good fortune, and hoping for the same luck himself, he had borrowed the dog Shiro; and now, just as he seemed on the point of finding what he sought, only a horrid smelling refuse heap had rewarded him for a morning's digging. Instead of blaming his own greed for his disappointment, he blamed the poor dog. He seized his spade, and with all his strength struck Shiro and killed him on the spot. He then threw the dog's body into the hole which he had dug in the hope of finding a treasure of gold coins, and covered it over with the earth. Then he returned to the house, telling no one, not even his wife, what he had done.

After waiting several days, as the dog Shiro did not return, his master began to grow anxious. Day after day went by and the good old man waited in vain. Then he went to his neighbor and asked him to give him back his dog. Without any shame or hesitation, the wicked neighbor answered that he had killed Shiro because of his bad behavior. At this dreadful news Shiro's master wept many sad and bitter tears. Great indeed, was his woful surprise, but he was too good and gentle to reproach his bad neighbor. Learning that Shiro was buried under the yenoki tree in the field, he asked the old man to give him the tree, in remembrance of his poor dog Shiro.

Even the cross old neighbor could not refuse such a simple request, so he consented to give the old man the tree under which Shiro lay buried. Shiro's master then cut the tree down and carried it home. Out of the trunk he made a mortar. In this his wife put some rice, and he began to pound it with the intention of making a festival to the memory of his dog Shiro.

A strange thing happened! His wife put the rice into the mortar, and no sooner had he begun to pound it to make the cakes, than it began to increase in quantity gradually till it was about five times the original amount, and the cakes were turned out of the mortar as if an invisible hand were at work.

When the old man and his wife saw this, they understood that it was a reward to them from Shiro for their faithful love to him. They tasted the cakes and found them nicer than any other food. So from this time they never troubled about food, for they lived upon the cakes with which the mortar never ceased to supply them.

The greedy neighbor, hearing of this new piece of good luck, was filled with envy as before, and called on the old man and asked leave to borrow the wonderful mortar for a short time, pretending that he, too, sorrowed for the death of Shiro, and wished to make cakes for a festival to the dog's memory.

The old man did not in the least wish to lend it to his cruel neighbor, but he was too kind to refuse. So the envious man carried home the mortar, but he never brought it back.

Several days passed, and Shiro's master waited in vain for the mortar, so he went to call on the borrower, and asked him to be good enough to return the mortar if he had finished with it. He found him sitting by a big fire made of pieces of wood. On the ground lay what looked very much like pieces of a broken mortar. In answer to the old man's inquiry, the wicked neighbor answered haughtily:

"Have you come to ask me for your mortar? I broke it to pieces, and now I am making a fire of the wood, for when I tried to pound cakes in it only some horrid smelling stuff came out."

The good old man said:

"I am very sorry for that. It is a great pity you did not ask me for the cakes if you wanted them. I would have given you as many as ever you wanted. Now please give me the ashes of the mortar, as I wish to keep them in remembrance of my dog."

The neighbor consented at once, and the old man carried home a basket full of ashes.

Not long after this the old man accidentally scattered

some of the ashes made by the burning of the mortar on the trees of his garden. A wonderful thing happened!

It was late in autumn and all the trees had shed their leaves, but no sooner did the ashes touch their branches than the cherry trees, the plum trees, and all other blossoming shrubs burst into bloom, so that the old man's garden was suddenly transformed into a beautiful picture of spring. The old man's delight knew no bounds, and he carefully preserved the remaining ashes.

The story of the old man's garden spread far and wide, and people from far and near came to see the wonderful sight.

One day, soon after this, the old man heard some one knocking at his door, and going to the porch to see who it was he was surprised to see a Knight standing there. This Knight told him that he was a retainer of a great Daimio (Earl); that one of the favorite cherry trees in this nobleman's garden had withered, and that though every one in his service had tried all manner of means to revive it, none took effect. The Knight was sore perplexed when he saw what great displeasure the loss of his favorite cherry tree caused the Daimio. At this point, fortunately, they had heard that there was a wonderful old man who could make withered trees to blossom, and that his Lord had sent him to ask the old man to come to him.

"And," added the Knight, "I shall be very much obliged if you will come at once."

The good old man was greatly surprised at what he heard, but respectfully followed the Knight to the nobleman's Palace.

The Daimio, who had been impatiently awaiting the old man's coming, as soon as he saw him asked him at once:

"Are you the old man who can make withered trees flower even out of season?"

The old man made an obeisance, and replied:

"I am that old man!"

Then the Daimio said:

"You must make that dead cherry tree in my garden blossom again by means of your famous ashes. I shall look on."

Then they all went into the garden—the Daimio and his retainers and the ladies-in waiting, who carried the Daimio's sword.

The old man now tucked up his kimono and made ready to climb the tree. Saying "Excuse me," he took the pot of ashes which he had brought with him, and began to climb the tree, every one watching his movements with great interest.

At last he climbed to the spot where the tree divided into two great branches, and taking up his position here, the old man sat down and scattered the ashes right and left all over the branches and twigs.

Wonderful, indeed, was the result! The withered tree at once burst into full bloom! The Daimio was so transported with joy that he looked as if he would go mad. He rose to his feet and spread out his fan, calling the old man down from the tree. He himself gave the old man a wine cup filled with the best SAKE, and rewarded him with much silver and gold and many other precious things. The Daimio ordered that henceforth the old man should call himself by the name of Hana-Sa-ka-Jijii, or "The Old Man who makes the Trees to Blossom," and that henceforth all were to recognize him by this name, and he sent him home with great honor.

The wicked neighbor, as before, heard of the good old man's fortune, and of all that had so auspiciously befallen him, and he could not suppress all the envy and jealousy that filled his heart. He called to mind how he had failed in his attempt to find the gold coins, and then in making the magic cakes; this time surely he must succeed if he imitated the old man, who made withered trees to flower simply by sprinkling ashes on them. This would be the simplest task of all.

So he set to work and gathered together all the ashes which remained in the fire-place from the burning of the wonderful mortar. Then he set out in the hope of finding some great man to employ him, calling out loudly as he went along:

"Here comes the wonderful man who can make withered trees blossom! Here comes the old man who can make dead trees blossom!"

The Daimio in his Palace heard this cry, and said:

"That must be the Hana-Saka-Jijii passing. I have nothing to do to-day. Let him try his art again; it will amuse me to look on."

So the retainers went out and brought in the impostor before their Lord. The satisfaction of false old man can now be imagined.

But the Daimio looking at him, thought it strange that he was not at all like the old man he had seen before, so he asked him:

"Are you the man whom I named Hana-Saka-Jijii?"

And the envious neighbor answered with a lie:

"Yes, my Lord!"

"That is strange!" said the Daimio. "I thought there was only one Hana-Saka-Jijii in the world! Has he now some disciples?"

"I am the true Hana-Saka-Jijii. The one who came to you before was only my disciple!" replied the old man again.

"Then you must be more skillful than the other. Try what you can do and let me see!"

The envious neighbor, with the Daimio and his Court following, then went into the garden, and approaching a dead tree, took out a handful of the ashes which he carried with him, and scattered them over the tree.

But not only did the tree not burst into flower, but not even a bud came forth. Thinking that he had not used enough ashes, the old man took handfuls and again sprinkled them over the withered tree. But all to no effect. After trying several times, the ashes were blown into the Daimio's eyes. This made him very angry, and he ordered his retainers to arrest the false Hana-Saka-Jijii at once and put him in prison for an impostor. From this imprisonment the wicked old man was never freed. Thus did he meet with punishment at last for all his evil doings.

The good old man, however, with the treasure of gold coins which Shiro had found for him, and with all the gold and the silver which the Daimio had showered on him, became a rich and prosperous man in his old age, and lived a long and happy life, beloved and respected by all.

THE JELLY FISH AND THE MONKEY

Long, long ago, in old Japan, the Kingdom of the Sea was governed by a wonderful King. He was called Rin Jin, or the Dragon King of the Sea. His power was immense, for he was the ruler of all sea creatures both great and small, and in his keeping were the Jewels of the Ebb and Flow of the Tide. The Jewel of the Ebbing Tide when thrown into the ocean caused the sea to recede from the land, and the Jewel of the Flowing Tide made the waves to rise mountains high and to flow in upon the shore like a tidal wave.

The Palace of Rin Jin was at the bottom of the sea, and was so beautiful that no one has ever seen anything like it even in dreams. The walls were of coral, the roof of jadestone and chrysoprase, and the floors were of the finest mother-of-pearl. But the Dragon King, in spite of his wide-spreading Kingdom, his beautiful Palace and all its wonders, and his power which none disputed throughout the whole sea, was not at all happy, for he reigned alone. At last he thought that if he married he would not only be happier, but also more powerful. So he decided to take a wife. Calling all his fish retainers together, he chose several of them as ambassadors to go through the sea and seek for a young Dragon Princess who would be his bride.

At last they returned to the Palace bringing with them a lovely young dragon. Her scales were of glittering green like the wings of summer beetles, her eyes threw out glances of fire, and she was dressed in gorgeous robes. All the jewels of the sea worked in with embroidery adorned them.

The King fell in love with her at once, and the wedding ceremony was celebrated with great splendor. Every living thing in the sea, from the great whales down to the little shrimps, came in shoals to offer their congratulations to the bride and bridegroom and to wish them a long and prosperous life. Never had there been such an assemblage or such gay festivities in the Fish-World before. The train of bearers who carried the bride's possessions to her new home seemed to reach across the waves from one end of the sea to the other. Each fish carried a phosphorescent lantern and was dressed in ceremonial robes, gleaming blue and pink and silver; and the waves as they rose and fell and broke that night seemed to be rolling masses of white and green fire, for the phosphorus shone with double brilliancy in honor of the event.

Now for a time the Dragon King and his bride lived very happily. They loved each other dearly, and the bridegroom day after day took delight in showing his bride all the wonders and treasures of his coral Palace, and she was never tired of wandering with him through its vast halls and gardens. Life seemed to them both like a long summer's day.

Two months passed in this happy way, and then the Dragon Queen fell ill and was obliged to stay in bed. The King was sorely troubled when he saw his precious bride so ill, and at once sent for the fish doctor to come and give her some medicine. He gave special orders to the servants to nurse her carefully and to wait upon her with diligence, but in spite of all the nurses' assiduous care and the medicine that the doctor prescribed, the young Queen showed no signs of recovery, but grew daily worse.

Then the Dragon King interviewed the doctor and blamed him for not curing the Queen. The doctor was alarmed at Rin Jin's evident displeasure, and excused his want of skill by saying that although he knew the right kind of medicine to give the invalid, it was impossible to find it in the sea.

"Do you mean to tell me that you can't get the medicine here?" asked the Dragon King.

"It is just as you say!" said the doctor.

"Tell me what it is you want for the Queen?" demanded Rin Jin.

"I want the liver of a live monkey!" answered the doctor.

"The liver of a live monkey! Of course that will be most difficult to get," said the King.

"If we could only get that for the Queen, Her Majesty would soon recover," said the doctor.

"Very well, that decides it; we MUST get it somehow or other. But where are we most likely to find a monkey?" asked the King.

Then the doctor told the Dragon King that some distance to the south there was a Monkey Island where a great many monkeys lived.

"If only you could capture one of these monkeys?" said the doctor.

"How can any of my people capture a monkey?" said the Dragon King, greatly puzzled. "The monkeys live on dry land, while we live in the water; and out of our element we are quite powerless! I don't see what we can do!"

"That has been my difficulty too," said the doctor. "But amongst your innumerable servants you surely can find one who can go on shore for that express purpose!"

"Something must be done," said the King, and calling his chief steward he consulted him on the matter.

The chief steward thought for some time, and then, as if struck by a sudden thought, said joyfully:

"I know what we must do! There is the kurage (jelly fish).

He is certainly ugly to look at, but he is proud of being able to walk on land with his four legs like a tortoise. Let us send him to the Island of Monkeys to catch one."

The jelly fish was then summoned to the King's presence, and was told by His Majesty what was required of him.

The jelly fish, on being told of the unexpected mission which was to be intrusted to him, looked very troubled, and said that he had never been to the island in question, and as he had never had any experience in catching monkeys he was afraid that he would not be able to get one.

"Well," said the chief steward, "if you depend on your strength or dexterity you will never catch a monkey. The only way is to play a trick on one!"

"How can I play a trick on a monkey? I don't know how to do it," said the perplexed jelly fish.

"This is what you must do," said the wily chief steward. "When you approach the Island of Monkeys and meet some of them, you must try to get very friendly with one. Tell him that you are a servant of the Dragon King, and invite him to come and visit you and see the Dragon King's Palace. Try and describe to him as vividly as you can the grandeur of the Palace and the wonders of the sea so as to arouse his curiosity and make him long to see it all!"

"But how am I to get the monkey here? You know monkeys don't swim?" said the reluctant jelly fish.

"You must carry him on your back. What is the use of your shell if you can't do that!" said the chief steward.

"Won't he be very heavy?" queried kurage again.

"You mustn't mind that, for you are working for the Dragon King," replied the chief steward.

"I will do my best then," said the jelly fish, and he swam

away from the Palace and started off towards the Monkey Island. Swimming swiftly he reached his destination in a few hours, and landed by a convenient wave upon the shore. On looking round he saw not far away a big pine-tree with drooping branches and on one of those branches was just what he was looking for—a live monkey.

"I'm in luck!" thought the jelly fish. "Now I must flatter the creature and try to entice him to come back with me to the Palace, and my part will be done!"

So the jelly fish slowly walked towards the pine-tree. In those ancient days the jelly fish had four legs and a hard shell like a tortoise. When he got to the pine-tree he raised his voice and said:

"How do you do, Mr. Monkey? Isn't it a lovely day?"

"A very fine day," answered the monkey from the tree. "I have never seen you in this part of the world before. Where have you come from and what is your name?"

"My name is kurage or jelly fish. I am one of the servants of the Dragon King. I have heard so much of your beautiful island that I have come on purpose to see it," answered the jelly fish.

"I am very glad to see you," said the monkey.

"By the bye," said the jelly fish, "have you ever seen the Palace of the Dragon King of the Sea where I live?"

"I have often heard of it, but I have never seen it!" answered the monkey.

"Then you ought most surely to come. It is a great pity for you to go through life without seeing it. The beauty of the Palace is beyond all description—it is certainly to my mind the most lovely place in the world," said the jelly fish.

"Is it so beautiful as all that?" asked the monkey in astonishment.

Then the jelly fish saw his chance, and went on describing to the best of his ability the beauty and grandeur of the Sea King's Palace, and the wonders of the garden with its curious trees of white, pink and red coral, and the still more curious fruits like great jewels hanging on the branches. The monkey grew more and more interested, and as he listened he came down the tree step by step so as not to lose a word of the wonderful story.

"I have got him at last!" thought the jelly fish, but aloud he said:

"Mr. Monkey. I must now go back. As you have never seen the Palace of the Dragon King, won't you avail yourself of this splendid opportunity by coming with me? I shall then be able to act as guide and show you all the sights of the sea, which will be even more wonderful to you—a land-lubber."

"I should love to go," said the monkey, "but how am I to cross the water! I can't swim, as you surely know!"

"There is no difficulty about that. I can carry you on my back."

"That will be troubling you too much," said the monkey.

"I can do it quite easily. I am stronger than I look, so you needn't hesitate," said the jelly fish, and taking the monkey on his back he stepped into the sea.

"Keep very still, Mr. monkey," said the jelly fish. "You mustn't fall into the sea; I am responsible for your safe arrival at the King's Palace."

"Please don't go so fast, or I am sure I shall fall off," said the monkey.

Thus they went along, the jelly fish skimming through the waves with the monkey sitting on his back. When they were about half-way, the jelly fish, who knew very little of anatomy, began to wonder if the monkey had his liver with him or not!

"Mr. Monkey, tell me, have you such a thing as a liver with you?"

The monkey was very much surprised at this queer question, and asked what the jelly fish wanted with a liver.

"That is the most important thing of all," said the stupid jelly fish, "so as soon as I recollected it, I asked you if you had yours with you?"

"Why is my liver so important to you?" asked the monkey.

"Oh! you will learn the reason later," said the jelly fish.

The monkey grew more and more curious and suspicious, and urged the jelly fish to tell him for what his liver was wanted, and ended up by appealing to his hearer's feelings by saying that he was very troubled at what he had been told.

Then the jelly fish, seeing how anxious the monkey looked, was sorry for him, and told him everything. How the Dragon Queen had fallen ill, and how the doctor had said that only the liver of a live monkey would cure her, and how the Dragon King had sent him to find one.

"Now I have done as I was told, and as soon as we arrive at the Palace the doctor will want your liver, so I feel sorry for you!" said the silly jelly fish.

The poor monkey was horrified when he learnt all this, and very angry at the trick played upon him. He trembled with fear at the thought of what was in store for him.

But the monkey was a clever animal, and he thought it the wisest plan not to show any sign of the fear he felt, so he tried to calm himself and to think of some way by which he might escape.

"The doctor means to cut me open and then take my liver out! Why I shall die!" thought the monkey. At last a bright thought struck him, so he said quite cheerfully to the jelly fish:

"What a pity it was, Mr. Jelly Fish, that you did not speak of this before we left the island!"

"If I had told why I wanted you to accompany me you would certainly have refused to come," answered the jelly fish.

"You are quite mistaken," said the monkey. "Monkeys can very well spare a liver or two, especially when it is wanted for the Dragon Queen of the Sea. If I had only guessed of what you were in need. I should have presented you with one without waiting to be asked. I have several livers. But the greatest pity is, that as you did not speak in time, I have left all my livers hanging on the pine-tree."

"Have you left your liver behind you?" asked the jelly fish.

"Yes," said the cunning monkey, "during the daytime I usually leave my liver hanging up on the branch of a tree, as it is very much in the way when I am climbing about from tree to tree. To-day, listening to your interesting conversation, I quite forgot it, and left it behind when I came off with you. If only you had spoken in time I should have remembered it, and should have brought it along with me!"

The jelly fish was very disappointed when he heard this, for he believed every word the monkey said. The monkey was of no good without a liver. Finally the jelly fish stopped and told the monkey so.

"Well," said the monkey, "that is soon remedied. I am really sorry to think of all your trouble; but if you will only take me back to the place where you found me, I shall soon be able to get my liver."

The jelly fish did not at all like the idea of going all the way back to the island again; but the monkey assured him that if he would be so kind as to take him back he would get his very best liver, and bring it with him the next time. Thus persuaded, the jelly fish turned his course towards the Monkey Island once more.

No sooner had the jelly fish reached the shore than the sly monkey landed, and getting up into the pine-tree where the jelly fish had first seen him, he cut several capers amongst the branches with joy at being safe home again, and then looking down at the jelly fish said:

"So many thanks for all the trouble you have taken! Please present my compliments to the Dragon King on your return!"

The jelly fish wondered at this speech and the mocking tone in which it was uttered. Then he asked the monkey if it wasn't his intention to come with him at once after getting his liver.

The monkey replied laughingly that he couldn't afford to lose his liver: it was too precious.

"But remember your promise!" pleaded the jelly fish, now very discouraged.

"That promise was false, and anyhow it is now broken!" answered the monkey. Then he began to jeer at the jelly fish and told him that he had been deceiving him the whole time; that he had no wish to lose his life, which he certainly would have done had he gone on to the Sea King's Palace to the old doctor waiting for him, instead of persuading the jelly fish to return under false pretenses.

"Of course, I won't GIVE you my liver, but come and get

it if you can!" added the monkey mockingly from the tree.

There was nothing for the jelly fish to do now but to re-pent of his stupidity, and to return to the Dragon King of the Sea and to confess his failure, so he started sadly and slowly to swim back. The last thing he heard as he glided away, leaving the island behind him, was the monkey laughing at him.

Meanwhile the Dragon King, the doctor, the chief stew-ard, and all the servants were waiting impatiently for the re-turn of the jelly fish. When they caught sight of him approach-ing the Palace, they hailed him with delight. They began to thank him profusely for all the trouble he had taken in going to Monkey Island, and then they asked him where the monkey was.

Now the day of reckoning had come for the jelly fish. He quaked all over as he told his story. How he had brought the monkey halfway over the sea, and then had stupidly let out the secret of his commission; how the monkey had deceived him by making him believe that he had left his liver behind him.

The Dragon King's wrath was great, and he at once gave orders that the jelly fish was to be severely punished. The pun-ishment was a horrible one. All the bones were to be drawn out from his living body, and he was to be beaten with sticks.

The poor jelly fish, humiliated and horrified beyond all words, cried out for pardon. But the Dragon King's order had to be obeyed. The servants of the Palace forthwith each brought out a stick and surrounded the jelly fish, and after pulling out his bones they beat him to a flat pulp, and then took him out beyond the Palace gates and threw him into the water. Here he was left to suffer and repent his foolish chatter-ing, and to grow accustomed to his new state of bonelessness.

From this story it is evident that in former times the jelly fish once had a shell and bones something like a tortoise, but, ever since the Dragon King's sentence was carried out on the ancestor of the jelly fishes, his descendants have all been soft and boneless just as you see them to-day thrown up by the waves high upon the shores of Japan.

THE QUARREL OF THE MONKEY AND THE CRAB

Long, long ago, one bright autumn day in Japan, it happened, that a pink-faced monkey and a yellow crab were playing together along the bank of a river. As they were running about, the crab found a rice-dumpling and the monkey a persimmon-seed.

The crab picked up the rice-dumpling and showed it to the monkey, saying:

"Look what a nice thing I have found!"

Then the monkey held up his persimmon-seed and said:

"I also have found something good! Look!"

Now though the monkey is always very fond of persimmon fruit, he had no use for the seed he had just found. The persimmon-seed is as hard and uneatable as a stone. He, therefore, in his greedy nature, felt very envious of the crab's nice dumpling, and he proposed an exchange. The crab naturally did not see why he should give up his prize for a hard stone-like seed, and would not consent to the monkey's proposition.

Then the cunning monkey began to persuade the crab, saying:

"How unwise you are not to think of the future! Your rice-dumpling can be eaten now, and is certainly much bigger than my seed; but if you sow this seed in the ground it will soon grow and become a great tree in a few years, and bear an abundance of fine ripe persimmons year after year. If only I could show it to you then with the yellow fruit hanging on its branches! Of course, if you don't believe me I shall sow it myself; though I am sure, later on, you will be very sorry that you did not take my advice."

The simple-minded crab could not resist the monkey's clever persuasion. He at last gave in and consented to the monkey's proposal, and the exchange was made. The greedy monkey soon gobbled up the dumpling, and with great reluctance gave up the persimmon-seed to the crab. He would have liked to keep that too, but he was afraid of making the crab angry and of being pinched by his sharp scissor-like claws. They then separated, the monkey going home to his forest trees and the crab to his stones along the river-side. As soon as the crab reached home he put the persimmon-seed in the ground as the monkey had told him.

In the following spring the crab was delighted to see the shoot of a young tree push its way up through the ground. Each year it grew bigger, till at last it blossomed one spring, and in the following autumn bore some fine large persimmons. Among the broad smooth green leaves the fruit hung like golden balls, and as they ripened they mellowed to a deep orange. It was the little crab's pleasure to go out day by day and sit in the sun and put out his long eyes in the same way as a snail puts out its horn, and watch the persimmons ripening to perfection.

"How delicious they will be to eat!" he said to himself.

At last, one day, he knew the persimmons must be quite ripe and he wanted very much to taste one. He made several attempts to climb the tree, in the vain hope of reaching one of the beautiful persimmons hanging above him; but he failed each time, for a crab's legs are not made for climbing trees but only for running along the ground and over stones, both of which he can do most cleverly. In his dilemma he thought of his old playmate the monkey, who, he knew, could climb trees better than any one else in the world. He determined to ask the monkey to help him, and set out to find him.

Running crab-fashion up the stony river bank, over the pathways into the shadowy forest, the crab at last found the monkey taking an afternoon nap in his favorite pine-tree, with his tail curled tight around a branch to prevent him from falling off in his dreams. He was soon wide awake, however, when he heard himself called, and eagerly listening to what the crab told him. When he heard that the seed which he had long ago exchanged for a rice-dumpling had grown into a tree and was now bearing good fruit, he was delighted, for he at once devised a cunning plan which would give him all the persimmons for himself.

He consented to go with the crab to pick the fruit for him. When they both reached the spot, the monkey was astonished to see what a fine tree had sprung from the seed, and with what a number of ripe persimmons the branches were loaded.

He quickly climbed the tree and began to pluck and eat, as fast as he could, one persimmon after another. Each time he chose the best and ripest he could find, and went on eating till he could eat no more. Not one would he give to the poor hungry crab waiting below, and when he had finished there was little but the hard, unripe fruit left.

You can imagine the feelings of the poor crab after waiting patiently, for so long as he had done, for the tree to grow and the fruit to ripen, when he saw the monkey devouring all the good persimmons. He was so disappointed that he ran round and round the tree calling to the monkey to remember his promise. The monkey at first took no notice of the crab's complaints, but at last he picked out the hardest, greenest persimmon he could find and aimed it at the crab's head. The persimmon is as hard as stone when it is unripe. The monkey's missile struck home and the crab was sorely hurt by the blow. Again and again, as fast as he could pick them, the monkey pulled off the hard persimmons and threw them at the defenseless crab till he dropped dead, covered with wounds all over his body. There he lay a pitiful sight at the foot of the tree he had himself planted.

When the wicked monkey saw that he had killed the crab he ran away from the spot as fast as he could, in fear and trembling, like a coward as he was.

Now the crab had a son who had been playing with a friend not far from the spot where this sad work had taken place. On the way home he came across his father dead, in a most dreadful condition—his head was smashed and his shell broken in several places, and around his body lay the unripe persimmons which had done their deadly work. At this dreadful sight the poor young crab sat down and wept.

But when he had wept for some time he told himself that this crying would do no good; it was his duty to avenge his father's murder, and this he determined to do. He looked about for some clue which would lead him to discover the murderer. Looking up at the tree he noticed that the best fruit had gone, and that all around lay bits of peel and numerous seeds strewn on the ground as well as the unripe persimmons which had evidently been thrown at his father. Then he understood that the monkey was the murderer, for he now remembered that his father had once told him the story of the rice-dumpling and the persimmon-seed. The young crab knew that monkeys liked persimmons above all other fruit, and he felt sure that his greed for the coveted fruit had been the cause of the old crab's death. Alas!

He at first thought of going to attack the monkey at once, for he burned with rage. Second thoughts, however, told him that this was useless, for the monkey was an old and cunning animal and would be hard to overcome. He must meet cunning with cunning and ask some of his friends to help him, for he knew it would be quite out of his power to kill him alone.

The young crab set out at once to call on the mortar, his father's old friend, and told him of all that had happened. He besought the mortar with tears to help him avenge his father's death. The mortar was very sorry when he heard the woful tale and promised at once to help the young crab punish the monkey to death. He warned him that he must be very careful in what he did, for the monkey was a strong and cunning enemy. The mortar now sent to fetch the bee and the chestnut (also the crab's old friends) to consult them about the matter. In a short time the bee and the chestnut arrived. When they were told all the details of the old crab's death and of the monkey's wickedness and greed, they both gladly consented to help the young crab in his revenge.

After talking for a long time as to the ways and means of carrying out their plans they separated, and Mr. Mortar went home with the young crab to help him bury his poor father.

While all this was taking place the monkey was congratulating himself (as the wicked often do before their punishment comes upon them) on all he had done so neatly. He thought it quite a fine thing that he had robbed his friend of all his ripe persimmons and then that he had killed him. Still, smile as hard as he might, he could not banish altogether the fear of the consequences should his evil deeds be discovered. IF he were found out (and he told himself that this could not be for he had escaped unseen) the crab's family would be sure to bear him hatred and seek to take revenge on him. So he would not go out, and kept himself at home for several days. He found this kind of life, however, extremely dull, accustomed as he was to the free life of the woods, and at last he said:

"No one knows that it was I who killed the crab! I am sure that the old thing breathed his last before I left him. Dead crabs have no mouths! Who is there to tell that I am the murderer? Since no one knows, what is the use of shutting myself up and brooding over the matter? What is done cannot be undone!"

With this he wandered out into the crab settlement and crept about as slyly as possible near the crab's house and tried to hear the neighbors' gossip round about. He wanted to find out what the crabs were saving about their chief's death, for the old crab had been the chief of the tribe. But he heard nothing and said to himself:

"They are all such fools that they don't know and don't care who murdered their chief!"

Little did he know in his so-called "monkey's wisdom" that this seeming unconcern was part of the young crab's plan. He purposely pretended not to know who killed his father, and also to believe that he had met his death through his own fault. By this means he could the better keep secret the revenge on the monkey, which he was meditating.

So the monkey returned home from his walk quite content. He told himself he had nothing now to fear.

One fine day, when the monkey was sitting at home, he was surprised by the appearance of a messenger from the young crab. While he was wondering what this might mean, the messenger bowed before him and said:

"I have been sent by my master to inform you that his father died the other day in falling from a persimmon tree while trying to climb the tree after fruit. This, being the seventh day, is the first anniversary after his death, and my master has prepared a little festival in his father's honor, and bids you come to participate in it as you were one of his best friends. My master hopes you will honor his house with your kind visit."

When the monkey heard these words he rejoiced in his inmost heart, for all his fears of being suspected were now at rest. He could not guess that a plot had just been set in motion against him. He pretended to be very surprised at the news of the crab's death, and said:

"I am, indeed, very sorry to hear of your chief's death. We were great friends as you know. I remember that we once exchanged a rice-dumpling for a persimmon-seed. It grieves me much to think that that seed was in the end the cause of his death. I accept your kind invitation with many thanks. I shall be delighted to do honor to my poor old friend!" And he screwed some false tears from his eyes.

The messenger laughed inwardly and thought, "The wicked monkey is now dropping false tears, but within a short time he shall shed real ones." But aloud he thanked the monkey politely and went home.

When he had gone, the wicked monkey laughed aloud at what he thought was the young crab's innocence, and without the least feeling began to look forward to the feast to be held that day in honor of the dead crab, to which he had been invited. He changed his dress and set out solemnly to visit the young crab.

He found all the members of the crab's family and his relatives waiting to receive and welcome him. As soon as the bows of meeting were over they led him to a hall. Here the young chief mourner came to receive him. Expressions of condolence and thanks were exchanged between them, and then they all sat down to a luxurious feast and entertained the monkey as the guest of honor.

The feast over, he was next invited to the tea-ceremony room to drink a cup of tea. When the young crab had conducted the monkey to the tearoom he left him and retired. Time passed and still he did not return. At last the monkey became impatient. He said to himself:

"This tea ceremony is always a very slow affair. I am tired of waiting so long. I am very thirsty after drinking so much sake at the dinner!"

He then approached the charcoal fire-place and began to pour out some hot water from the kettle boiling there, when something burst out from the ashes with a great pop and hit the monkey right in the neck. It was the chestnut, one of the crab's friends, who had hidden himself in the fireplace. The monkey, taken by surprise, jumped backward, and then started to run out of the room.

The bee, who was hiding outside the screens, now flew out and stung him on the cheek. The monkey was in great pain, his neck was burned by the chestnut and his face badly stung by the bee, but he ran on screaming and chattering with rage.

Now the stone mortar had hidden himself with several other stones on the top of the crab's gate, and as the monkey ran underneath, the mortar and all fell down on the top of the monkey's head. Was it possible for the monkey to bear the weight of the mortar falling on him from the top of the gate? He lay crushed and in great pain, quite unable to get up. As he lay there helpless the young crab came up, and, holding his great claw scissors over the monkey, he said:

"Do you now remember that you murdered my father?"

"Then you—are—my—enemy?" gasped the monkey brokenly.

"Of course," said the young crab.

"It—was—your—father's—fault—not—mine!" gasped the unrepentant monkey.

"Can you still lie? I will soon put an end to your breath!" and with that he cut off the monkey's head with his pitcher claws. Thus the wicked monkey met his well-merited punishment, and the young crab avenged his father's death.

This is the end of the story of the monkey, the crab, and the persimmon-seed.

THE WHITE HARE AND THE CROCODILES

Long, long ago, when all the animals could talk, there lived in the province of Inaba in Japan, a little white hare. His home was on the island of Oki, and just across the sea was the mainland of Inaba.

Now the hare wanted very much to cross over to Inaba. Day after day he would go out and sit on the shore and look longingly over the water in the direction of Inaba, and day after day he hoped to find some way of getting across.

One day as usual, the hare was standing on the beach, looking towards the mainland across the water, when he saw a great crocodile swimming near the island.

"This is very lucky!" thought the hare. "Now I shall be able to get my wish. I will ask the crocodile to carry me across the sea!"

But he was doubtful whether the crocodile would consent to do what wanted. So he thought instead of asking a favor he would try to get what he wanted by a trick.

So with a loud voice he called to the crocodile, and said:

"Oh, Mr. Crocodile, isn't it a lovely day?"

The crocodile, who had come out all by itself that day to enjoy the bright sunshine, was just beginning to feel a bit lonely when the hare's cheerful greeting broke the silence. The crocodile swam nearer the shore, very pleased to hear some one speak.

"I wonder who it was that spoke to me just now! Was it you, Mr. Hare? You must be very lonely all by yourself!"

"Oh, no, I am not at all lonely," said the hare, "but as it was such a fine day I came out here to enjoy myself. Won't you stop and play with me a little while?"

The crocodile came out of the sea and sat on the shore, and the two played together for some time. Then the hare said:

"Mr. Crocodile, you live in the sea and I live on this island, and we do not often meet, so I know very little about you. Tell me, do you think the number of your company is greater than mine?"

"Of course, there are more crocodiles than hares," answered the crocodile. "Can you not see that for yourself? You live on this small island, while I live in the sea, which spreads through all parts of the world, so if I call together all the crocodiles who dwell in the sea you hares will be as nothing compared to us!" The crocodile was very conceited.

The hare, who meant to play a trick on the crocodile, said:

"Do you think it possible for you to call up enough crocodiles to form a line from this island across the sea to Inaba?"

The crocodile thought for a moment and then answered:

"Of course, it is possible."

"Then do try," said the artful hare, "and I will count the number from here!"

The crocodile, who was very simple-minded, and who hadn't the least idea that the hare intended to play a trick on him, agreed to do what the hare asked, and said:

"Wait a little while I go back into the sea and call my company together!"

The crocodile plunged into the sea and was gone for some time. The hare, meanwhile, waited patiently on the shore. At last the crocodile appeared, bringing with him a large number of other crocodiles.

"Look, Mr. Hare!" said the crocodile, "it is nothing for

my friends to form a line between here and Inaba. There are enough crocodiles to stretch from here even as far as China or India. Did you ever see so many crocodiles?"

Then the whole company of crocodiles arranged themselves in the water so as to form a bridge between the Island of Oki and the mainland of Inaba. When the hare saw the bridge of crocodiles, he said:

"How splendid! I did not believe this was possible. Now let me count you all! To do this, however, with your permission, I must walk over on your backs to the other side, so please be so good as not to move, or else I shall fall into the sea and be drowned!"

So the hare hopped off the island on to the strange bridge of crocodiles, counting as he jumped from one crocodile's back to the other:

"Please keep quite still, or I shall not be able to count. One, two, three, four, five, six, seven, eight, nine—"

Thus the cunning hare walked right across to the mainland of Inaba. Not content with getting his wish, he began to jeer at the crocodiles instead of thanking them, and said, as he leapt off the last one's back:

"Oh! you stupid crocodiles, now I have done with you!"

And he was just about to run away as fast as he could. But he did not escape so easily, for so soon as the crocodiles understood that this was a trick played upon them by the hare so as to enable him to cross the sea, and that the hare was now laughing at them for their stupidity, they became furiously angry and made up their minds to take revenge. So some of them ran after the hare and caught him. Then they all surrounded the poor little animal and pulled out all his fur. He cried out loudly and entreated them to spare him, but with each tuft of fur they pulled out they said:

"Serve you right!"

When the crocodiles had pulled out the last bit of fur, they threw the poor hare on the beach, and all swam away laughing at what they had done.

The hare was now in a pitiful plight, all his beautiful white fur had been pulled out, and his bare little body was quivering with pain and bleeding all over. He could hardly move, and all he could do was to lie on the beach quite help-less and weep over the misfortune that had befallen him. Not-withstanding that it was his own fault that had brought all this misery and suffering upon the white hare of Inaba, any one seeing the poor little creature could not help feeling sorry for him in his sad condition, for the crocodiles had been very cru-el in their revenge.

Just at this time a number of men, who looked like King's sons, happened to pass by, and seeing the hare lying on the beach crying, stopped and asked what was the matter.

The hare lifted up his head from between his paws, and answered them, saying:

"I had a fight with some crocodiles, but I was beaten, and they pulled out all my fur and left me to suffer here—that is why I am crying."

Now one of these young men had a bad and spiteful dis-position. But he feigned kindness, and said to the hare:

"I feel very sorry for you. If you will only try it, I know of a remedy which will cure your sore body. Go and bathe yourself in the sea, and then come and sit in the wind. This will make your fur grow again, and you will be just as you were before."

Then all the young men passed on. The hare was very pleased, thinking that he had found a cure. He went and bathed in the sea and then came out and sat where the wind could blow upon him.

But as the wind blew and dried him, his skin became drawn and hardened, and the salt increased the pain so much that he rolled on the sand in his agony and cried aloud.

Just then another King's son passed by, carrying a great bag on his back. He saw the hare, and stopped and asked why he was crying so loudly.

But the poor hare, remembering that he had been deceived by one very like the man who now spoke to him, did not answer, but continued to cry.

But this man had a kind heart, and looked at the hare very pityingly, and said:

"You poor thing! I see that your fur is all pulled out and that your skin is quite bare. Who can have treated you so cruelly?"

When the hare heard these kind words he felt very grateful to the man, and encouraged by his gentle manner the hare told him all that had befallen him. The little animal hid nothing from his friend, but told him frankly how he had played a trick on the crocodiles and how he had come across the bridge they had made, thinking that he wished to count their number: how he had jeered at them for their stupidity, and then how the crocodiles had revenged themselves on him. Then he went on to say how he had been deceived by a party of men who looked very like his kind friend: and the hare ended his long tale of woe by begging the man to give him some medicine that would cure him and make his fur grow again.

When the hare had finished his story, the man was full of pity towards him, and said:

"I am very sorry for all you have suffered, but remember,

it was only the consequence of the deceit you practiced on the crocodiles."

"I know," answered the sorrowful hare, "but I have repented and made up my mind never to use deceit again, so I beg you to show me how I may cure my sore body and make the fur grow again."

"Then I will tell you of a good remedy," said the man. "First go and bathe well in that pond over there and try to wash all the salt from your body. Then pick some of those kaba flowers that are growing near the edge of the water, spread them on the ground and roll yourself on them. If you do this the pollen will cause your fur to grow again, and you will be quite well in a little while."

The hare was very glad to be told what to do, so kindly. He crawled to the pond pointed out to him, bathed well in it, and then picked the kaba flowers growing near the water, and rolled himself on them.

To his amazement, even while he was doing this, he saw his nice white fur growing again, the pain ceased, and he felt just as he had done before all his misfortunes.

The hare was overjoyed at his quick recovery, and went hopping joyfully towards the young man who had so helped him, and kneeling down at his feet, said:

"I cannot express my thanks for all you have done for me! It is my earnest wish to do something for you in return. Please tell me who you are?"

"I am no King's son as you think me. I am a fairy, and my name is Okuni-nushi-no-Mikoto," answered the man, "and those beings who passed here before me are my brothers. They have heard of a beautiful Princess called Yakami who lives in this province of Inaba, and they are on their way to find her and to ask her to marry one of them. But on this expedition I am only an attendant, so I am walking behind them with this great big bag on my back."

The hare humbled himself before this great fairy Okuninushi-no-Mikoto, whom many in that part of the land worshiped as a god.

"Oh, I did not know that you were Okuni-nushi-no-Mikoto. How kind you have been to me! It is impossible to believe that that unkind fellow who sent me to bathe in the sea is one of your brothers. I am quite sure that the Princess, whom your brothers have gone to seek, will refuse to be the bride of any of them, and will prefer you for your goodness of heart. I am quite sure that you will win her heart without intending to do so, and she will ask to be your bride."

Okuni-nushi-no-Mikoto took no notice of what the hare said, but bidding the little animal goodby, went on his way quickly and soon overtook his brothers. He found them just entering the Princess's gate.

Just as the hare had said, the Princess could not be persuaded to become the bride of any of the brothers, but when she looked at the kind brother's face she went straight up to him and said:

"To you I give myself," and so they were married.

This is the end of the story. Okuni-nushi-no-Mikoto is worshiped by the people in some parts of Japan, as a god, and the hare has become famous as "The White Hare of Inaba." But what became of the crocodiles nobody knows.

THE STORY OF
PRINCE YAMATO TAKE

The insignia of the great Japanese Empire is composed of
three treasures which have been considered sacred, and
guarded with jealous care from time immemorial. These are
the Yatano-no-Kagami or the Mirror of Yata, the Yasaka-
mi-no-Magatama or the Jewel of Yasakami, and the Muraku-
mo-no-Tsurugi or the Sword of Murakumo.

Of these three treasures of the Empire, the sword of
Murakumo, afterwards known as Kusanagi-no-Tsrugugi, or
the grass-cleaving sword, is considered the most precious and
most highly to be honored, for it is the symbol of strength to
this nation of warriors and the talisman of invincibility for the
Emperor, while he holds it sacred in the shrine of his ancestors.

Nearly two thousand years ago this sword was kept at the
shrines of Ite, the temples dedicated to the worship of Amaterasu, the great and beautiful Sun Goddess from whom the
Japanese Emperors are said to be descended.

There is a story of knightly adventure and daring which
explains why the name of the sword was changed from that of
Murakumo to Kasanagi, which means grass clearing.

Once, many, many years ago, there was born a son to
the Emperor Keiko, the twelfth in descent from the great Jim-
mu, the founder of the Japanese dynasty. This Prince was the
second son of the Emperor Keiko, and he was named Yamato. From his childhood he proved himself to be of remarkable
strength, wisdom and courage, and his father noticed with
pride that he gave promise of great things, and he loved him
even more than he did his elder son.

Now when Prince Yamato had grown to manhood (in the olden days of Japanese history, a boy was considered to have reached man's estate at the early age of sixteen) the realm was much troubled by a band of outlaws whose chiefs were two brothers, Kumaso and Takeru. These rebels seemed to delight in rebelling against the King, in breaking the laws and defying all authority.

At last King Keiko ordered his younger son Prince Yamato to subdue the brigands and, if possible, to rid the land of their evil lives. Prince Yamato was only sixteen years of age, he had but reached his manhood according to the law, yet though he was such a youth in years he possessed the dauntless spirit of a warrior of fuller age and knew not what fear was. Even then there was no man who could rival him for courage and bold deeds, and he received his father's command with great joy.

He at once made ready to start, and great was the stir in the precincts of the Palace as he and his trusty followers gathered together and prepared for the expedition, and polished up their armor and donned it. Before he left his father's Court he went to pray at the shrine of Ise and to take leave of his aunt the Princess Yamato, for his heart was somewhat heavy at the thought of the dangers he had to face, and he felt that he needed the protection of his ancestress, Amaterasu, the Sun Goddess. The Princess his aunt came out to give him glad welcome, and congratulated him on being trusted with so great a mission by his father the King. She then gave him one of her gorgeous robes as a keepsake to go with him and to bring him good luck, saying that it would surely be of service to him on this adventure. She then wished him all success in his undertaking and bade him good speed.

The young Prince bowed low before his aunt, and received her gracious gift with much pleasure and many respectful bows.

"I will now set out," said the Prince, and returning to the Palace he put himself at the head of his troops. Thus cheered by his aunt's blessing, he felt ready for all that might befall, and marching through the land he went down to the Southern Island of Kiushiu, the home of the brigands.

Before many days had passed he reached the Southern Island, and then slowly but surely made his way to the head-quarters of the chiefs Kumaso and Takeru. He now met with great difficulties, for he found the country exceedingly wild and rough. The mountains were high and steep, the valleys dark and deep, and huge trees and bowlders of rock blocked up the road and stopped the progress of his army. It was all but impossible to go on.

Though the Prince was but a youth he had the wisdom of years, and, seeing that it was vain to try and lead his men further, he said to himself:

"To attempt to fight a battle in this impassable country unknown to my men only makes my task harder. We cannot clear the roads and fight as well. It is wiser for me to resort to stratagem and come upon my enemies unawares. In that way I may be able to kill them without much exertion."

So he now bade his army halt by the way. His wife, the Princess Ototachibana, had accompanied him, and he bade her bring him the robe his aunt the priestess of Ise had given him, and to help him attire himself as a woman. With her help he put on the robe, and let his hair down till it flowed over his shoulders. Ototachibana then brought him her comb, which he put in his black tresses, and then adorned himself with strings of strange jewels just as you see in the picture. When he had finished his unusual toilet, Ototachibana brought him her mirror. He smiled as he gazed at himself—the disguise was so perfect.

He hardly knew himself, so changed was he. All traces of the warrior had disappeared, and in the shining surface only a beautiful lady looked back at him.

Thus completely disguised, he set out for the enemy's camp alone. In the folds of his silk gown, next his strong heart, was hidden a sharp dagger.

The two chiefs Kumaso and Takeru wore sitting in their tent, resting in the cool of the evening, when the Prince approached. They were talking of the news which had recently been carried to them, that the King's son had entered their country with a large army determined to exterminate their band. They had both heard of the young warrior's renown, and for the first time in their wicked lives they felt afraid. In a pause in their talk they happened to look up, and saw through the door of the tent a beautiful woman robed in sumptuous garments coming towards them. Like an apparition of loveliness she appeared in the soft twilight. Little did they dream that it was their enemy whose coming they so dreaded who now stood before them in this disguise.

"What a beautiful woman! Where has she come from?" said the astonished Kumaso, forgetting war and council and everything as he looked at the gentle intruder.

He beckoned to the disguised Prince and bade him sit down and serve them with wine. Yamato Take felt his heart swell with a fierce glee for he now knew that his plan would succeed. However, he dissembled cleverly, and putting on a sweet air of shyness he approached the rebel chief with slow steps and eyes glancing like a frightened deer. Charmed to distraction by the girl's loveliness Kumaso drank cup after cup of wine for the pleasure of seeing her pour it out for him, till at last he was quite overcome with the quantity he had drunk.

This was the moment for which the brave Prince had been waiting. Flinging down the wine jar, he seized the tipsy and astonished Kumaso and quickly stabbed him to death with the dagger which he had secretly carried hidden in his breast.

Takeru, the brigand's brother, was terror-struck as soon as he saw what was happening and tried to escape, but Prince Yamato was too quick for him. Ere he could reach the tent door the Prince was at his heel, his garments were clutched by a hand of iron, and a dagger flashed before his eyes and he lay stabbed to the earth, dying but not yet dead.

"Wait one moment!" gasped the brigand painfully, and he seized the Prince's hand.

Yamato relaxed his hold somewhat and said.

"Why should I pause, thou villain?"

The brigand raised himself fearfully and said:

"Tell me from whence you come, and whom I have the honor of addressing? Hitherto I believed that my dead brother and I were the strongest men in the land, and that there was no one who could overcome us. Alone you have ventured into our stronghold, alone you have attacked and killed us! Surely you are more than mortal?"

Then the young Prince answered with a proud smile: "I am the son of the King and my name is Yamato, and I have been sent by my father as the avenger of evil to bring death to all rebels! No longer shall robbery and murder hold my people in terror!" and he held the dagger dripping red above the rebel's head.

"Ah," gasped the dying man with a great effort, "I have often heard of you. You are indeed a strong man to have so easily overcome us. Allow me to give you a new name. From henceforth you shall be known as Yamato Take. Our title I bequeath to you as the bravest man in Yamato."

And with these noble words, Takeru fell back and died.

The Prince having thus successfully put an end to his father's enemies in the world, was prepared to return to the capital. On the way back he passed through the province of Idum. Here he met with another outlaw named Idzumo Takeru who he knew had done much harm in the land. He again resorted to stratagem, and feigned friendship with the rebel under an assumed name. Having done this he made a sword of wood and jammed it tightly in the shaft of his own strong sword. This he purposedly buckled to his side and wore on every occasion when he expected to meet the third robber Takeru.

He now invited Takeru to the bank of the River Hinokawa, and persuaded him to try a swim with him in the cool refreshing waters of the river.

As it was a hot summer's day, the rebel was nothing loath to take a plunge in the river, while his enemy was still swimming down the stream the Prince turned back and landed with all possible haste. Unperceived, he managed to change swords, putting his wooden one in place of the keen steel sword of Takeru.

Knowing nothing of this, the brigand came up to the bank shortly. As soon as he had landed and donned his clothes, the Prince came forward and asked him to cross swords with him to prove his skill, saying:

"Let us two prove which is the better swordsman of the

two!"

The robber agreed with delight, feeling certain of victory, for he was famous as a fencer in his province and he did not know who his adversary was. He seized quickly what he thought was his sword and stood on guard to defend himself. Alas! for the rebel the sword was the wooden one of the young Prince and in vain Takeru tried to unsheathe it—it was jammed fast, not all his exerted strength could move it. Even if his efforts had been successful the sword would have been of no use to him for it was of wood. Yamato Take saw that his enemy was in his power, and swinging high the sword he had taken from Takeru he brought it down with great might and dexterity and cut off the robber's head.

In this way, sometimes by using his wisdom and sometimes by using his bodily strength, and at other times by resorting to craftiness, which was as much esteemed in those days as it is despised in these, he prevailed against all the King's foes one by one, and brought peace and rest to the land and the people.

When he returned to the capital the King praised him for his brave deeds, and held a feast in the Palace in honor of his safe coming home and presented him with many rare gifts. From this time forth the King loved him more than ever and would not let Yamato Take go from his side, for he said that his son was now as precious to him as one of his arms.

But the Prince was not allowed to live an idle life long. When he was about thirty years old, news was brought that the Ainu race, the aborigines of the islands of Japan, who had been conquered and pushed northwards by the Japanese, had rebelled in the Eastern provinces, and leaving the vicinity which had been allotted to them were causing great trouble in the land. The King decided that it was necessary to send an army to do battle with them and bring them to reason. But who was to lead the men?

Prince Yamato Take at once offered to go and bring the newly arisen rebels into subjection. Now as the King loved the Prince dearly, and could not bear to have him go out of his sight even for the length of one day, he was of course very loath to send him on his dangerous expedition. But in the whole army there was no warrior so strong or so brave as the Prince his son, so that His Majesty, unable to do otherwise, reluctantly complied with Yamato's wish.

When the time came for the Prince to start, the King gave him a spear called the Eight-Arms-Length-Spear of the Holly Tree (the handle was probably made from the wood of the holly tree), and ordered him to set out to subjugate the Eastern Barbarians as the Ainu were then called.

The Eight-Arms-Length-Spear of the Holly Tree of those old days, was prized by warriors just as much as the Standard or Banner is valued by a regiment in these modern days, when given by the King to his soldiers on the occasion of setting out for war.

The Prince respectfully and with great reverence received the King's spear, and leaving the capital, marched with his army to the East. On his way he visited first of all the temples of Ise for worship, and his aunt the Princess of Yamato and High Priestess came out to greet him. She it was who had given him her robe which had proved such a boon to him before in helping him to overcome and slay the brigands of the West.

He told her all that had happened to him, and of the great part her keepsake had played in the success of his previous undertaking, and thanked her very heartily. When she heard that he was starting out once again to do battle with his father's enemies, she went into the temple, and reappeared bearing a sword and a beautiful bag which she had made herself, and which was full of flints, which in those times people used instead of matches for making fire. These she presented to him as a parting gift.

The sword was the sword of Murakumo, one of the three sacred treasures which comprise the insignia of the Imperial House of Japan. No more auspicious talisman of luck and success could she have given her nephew, and she bade him use it in the hour of his greatest need.

Yamato Take now bade farewell to his aunt, and once more placing himself at the head of his men he marched to the farthest East through the province of Owari, and then he reached the province of Suruga. Here the governor welcomed the Prince right heartily and entertained him royally with many feasts. When these were over, the governor told his guest that his country was famous for its fine deer, and proposed a deer hunt for the Prince's amusement. The Prince was utterly deceived by the cordiality of his host, which was all feigned, and gladly consented to join in the hunt.

The governor then led the Prince to a wild and extensive plain where the grass grew high and in great abundance. Quite ignorant that the governor had laid a trap for him with the desire to compass his death, the Prince began to ride hard and hunt down the deer, when all of a sudden to his amazement he saw flames and smoke bursting out from the bush in front of him. Realizing his danger he tried to retreat, but no sooner did he turn his horse in the opposite direction than he saw that even there the prairie was on fire. At the same time the grass on his left and right burst into flames, and these began to spread swiftly towards him on all sides. He looked round for a chance of escape. There was none. He was surrounded by fire.

"This deer hunt was then only a cunning trick of the enemy!" said the Prince, looking round on the flames and the smoke that crackled and rolled in towards him on every side. "What a fool I was to be lured into this trap like a wild beast!" and he ground his teeth with rage as he thought of the governor's smiling treachery.

Dangerous as was his situation now, the Prince was not in the least confounded. In his dire extremity he remembered the gifts his aunt had given him when they parted, and it seemed to him as if she must, with prophetic foresight, have divined this hour of need. He coolly opened the flint-bag that his aunt had given him and set fire to the grass near him. Then drawing the sword of Murakumo from its sheath he set to work to cut down the grass on either side of him with all speed. He determined to die, if that were necessary, fighting for his life and not standing still waiting for death to come to him.

Strange to say the wind began to change and to blow from the opposite direction, and the fiercest portion of the burning bush which had hitherto threatened to come upon him was now blown right away from him, and the Prince, without even a scratch on his body or a single hair burned, lived to tell the tale of his wonderful escape, while the wind rising to a gale overtook the governor, and he was burned to death in the flames he had set alight to kill Yamato Take.

Now the Prince ascribed his escape entirely to the virtue of the sword of Murakumo, and to the protection of Amaterasu, the Sun Goddess of Ise, who controls the wind and all the elements and insures the safety of all who pray to her in the hour of danger. Lifting the precious sword he raised it above his head many times in token of his great respect, and as he did this he re-named it Kusanagi-no-Tsurugi or the Grass-Cleaving Sword, and the place where he set fire to the grass round him and escaped from death in the burning prairie, he called Yaidzu. To this day there is a spot along the great Tokaido railway named Yaidzu, which is said to be the very place where this thrilling event took place.

Thus did the brave Prince Yamato Take escape out of the snare laid for him by his enemy. He was full of resource and courage, and finally outwitted and subdued all his foes. Leaving Yaidzu he marched eastward, and came to the shore at Idzu from whence he wished to cross to Kadzusa.

In these dangers and adventures he had been followed by his faithful loving wife the Princess Ototachibana. For his sake she counted the weariness of the long journeys and the dangers of war as nothing, and her love for her warrior husband was so great that she felt well repaid for all her wanderings if she could but hand him his sword when he sallied forth to battle, or minister to his wants when he returned weary to the camp.

But the heart of the Prince was full of war and conquest and he cared little for the faithful Ototachibana. From long exposure in traveling, and from care and grief at her lord's coldness to her, her beauty had faded, and her ivory skin was burnt brown by the sun, and the Prince told her one day that her place was in the Palace behind the screens at home and not with him upon the warpath. But in spite of rebuffs and indifference on her husband's part, Ototachibana could not find it in her heart to leave him. But perhaps it would have been better for her if she had done so, for on the way to Idzu, when they came to Owari, her heart was well-nigh broken.

Here dwelt in a Palace shaded by pine-trees and approached by imposing gates, the Princess Miyadzu, beautiful as the cherry blossom in the blushing dawn of a spring morning. Her garments were dainty and bright, and her skin was white as snow, for she had never known what it was to be weary along the path of duty or to walk in the heat of a summer's sun. And the Prince was ashamed of his sunburnt wife in her travel-stained garments, and bade her remain behind while he went to visit the Princess Miyadzu. Day after day he spent hours in the gardens and the Palace of his new friend, thinking only of his pleasure, and caring little for his poor wife who remained behind to weep in the tent at the misery which had come into her life. Yet she was so faithful a wife, and her character so patient, that she never allowed a reproach to escape her lips, or a frown to mar the sweet sadness of her face, and she was ever ready with a smile to welcome her husband back or usher him forth wherever he went.

At last the day came when the Prince Yamato Take must depart for Idzu and cross over the sea to Kadzusa, and he bade his wife follow in his retinue as an attendant while he went to take a ceremonious farewell of the Princess Miyadzu. She came out to greet him dressed in gorgeous robes, and she seemed more beautiful than ever, and when Yamato Take saw her he forgot his wife, his duty, and everything except the joy of the idle present, and swore that he would return to Owari and marry her when the war was over. And as he looked up when he had said these words he met the large almond eyes of Ototachibana fixed full upon him in unspeakable sadness and wonder, and he knew that he had done wrong, but he hardened his heart and rode on, caring little for the pain he had caused her.

When they reached the seashore at Idzu his men sought for boats in which to cross the straits to Kadzusa, but it was difficult to find boats enough to allow all the soldiers to embark. Then the Prince stood on the beach, and in the pride of his strength he scoffed and said:

"This is not the sea! This is only a brook! Why do you men want so many boats? I could jump this if I would."

When at last they had all embarked and were fairly on their way across the straits, the sky suddenly clouded and a great storm arose. The waves rose mountains high, the wind howled, the lightning flashed and the thunder rolled, and the boat which held Ototachibana and the Prince and his men was tossed from crest to crest of the rolling waves, till it seemed that every moment must be their last and that they must all be swallowed up in the angry sea. For Kin Jin, the Dragon King of the Sea, had heard Yamato Take jeer, and had raised this terrible storm in anger, to show the scoffing Prince how awful the sea could be though it did but look like a brook.

The terrified crew lowered the sails and looked after the rudder, and worked for their dear lives' sake, but all in vain—the storm only seemed to increase in violence, and all gave themselves up for lost. Then the faithful Ototachibana rose, and forgetting all the grief that her husband had caused her, forgetting even that he had wearied of her, in the one great desire of her love to save him, she determined to sacrifice her life to rescue him from death if it were possible.

While the waves dashed over the ship and the wind whirled round them in fury she stood up and said:

"Surely all this has come because the Prince has angered Rin Jin, the God of the Sea, by his jesting. If so, I, Ototachibana, will appease the wrath of the Sea God who desires nothing less than my husband's life!"

Then addressing the sea she said:

"I will take the place of His Augustness, Yamato Take. I will now cast myself into your outraged depths, giving my life for his. Therefore hear me and bring him safely to the shore of Kadzusa."

With these words she leaped quickly into the boisterous sea, and the waves soon whirled her away and she was lost to sight. Strange to say, the storm ceased at once, and the sea became as calm and smooth as the matting on which the astonished onlookers were sitting. The gods of the sea were now appeased, and the weather cleared and the sun shone as on a summer's day.

Yamato Take soon reached the opposite shore and landed safely, even as his wife Ototachibana had prayed. His prowess in war was marvelous, and he succeeded after some time in conquering the Eastern Barbarians, the Ainu.

He ascribed his safe landing wholly to the faithfulness of his wife, who had so willingly and lovingly sacrificed herself in the hour of his utmost peril. His heart was softened at the remembrance of her, and he never allowed her to pass from his thoughts even for a moment. Too late had he learned to esteem the goodness of her heart and the greatness of her love for him.

As he was returning on his homeward way he came to the high pass of the Usui Toge, and here he stood and gazed at the wonderful prospect beneath him. The country, from this great elevation, all lay open to his sight, a vast panorama of mountain and plain and forest, with rivers winding like silver ribbons through the land; then far off he saw the distant sea, which shimmered like a luminous mist in the great distance, where Ototachibana had given her life for him, and as he turned towards it he stretched out his arms, and thinking of her love which he had scorned and his faithlessness to her, his heart burst out into a sorrowful and bitter cry:

"Azuma, Azuma, Ya!" (Oh! my wife, my wife!) And to this day there is a district in Tokio called Azuma, which commemorates the words of Prince Yamato Take, and the place where his faithful wife leapt into the sea to save him is still pointed out. So, though in life the Princess Ototachibana was unhappy, history keeps her memory green, and the story of her unselfishness and heroic death will never pass away.

Yamato Take had now fulfilled all his father's orders, he had subdued all rebels, and rid the land of all robbers and enemies to the peace, and his renown was great, for in the whole land there was no one who could stand up against him, he was so strong in battle and wise in council.

He was about to return straight for home by the way he had come, when the thought struck him that he would find it more interesting to take another route, so he passed through the province of Owari and came to the province of Omi.

When the Prince reached Omi he found the people in a state of great excitement and fear. In many houses as he passed along he saw the signs of mourning and heard loud lamentations. On inquiring the cause of this he was told that a terrible monster had appeared in the mountains, who daily came down from thence and made raids on the villages, devouring whoever he could seize. Many homes had been made desolate and the men were afraid to go out to their daily work in the fields, or the women to go to the rivers to wash their rice.

When Yamato Take heard this his wrath was kindled, and he said fiercely:

"From the western end of Kiushiu to the eastern corner of Yezo I have subdued all the King's enemies—there is no one who dares to break the laws or to rebel against the King. It is indeed a matter for wonder that here in this place, so near the capital, a wicked monster has dared to take up his abode and be the terror of the King's subjects. Not long shall it find pleasure in devouring innocent folk. I will start out and kill it at once."

With these words he set out for the Ibuki Mountain, where the monster was said to live. He climbed up a good distance, when all of a sudden, at a winding in the path, a monster serpent appeared before him and stopped the way.

"This must be the monster," said the Prince; "I do not need my sword for a serpent. I can kill him with my hands."

He thereupon sprang upon the serpent and tried to strangle it to death with his bare arms. It was not long before his prodigious strength gained the mastery and the serpent lay dead at his feet. Now a sudden darkness came over the mountain and rain began to fall, so that for the gloom and the rain the Prince could hardly see which way to take. In a short time, however, while he was groping his way down the pass, the weather cleared, and our brave hero was able to make his way quickly down the mountain.

When he got back he began to feel ill and to have burning pains in his feet, so he knew that the serpent had poisoned him. So great was his suffering that he could hardly move, much less walk, so he had himself carried to a place in the mountains famous for its hot mineral springs, which rose bubbling out of the earth, and almost boiling from the volcanic fires beneath.

Yamato Take bathed daily in these waters, and gradually he felt his strength come again, and the pains left him, till at last one day he found with great joy that he was quite recovered. He now hastened to the temples of Ise, where you will remember that he prayed before undertaking this long expedition. His aunt, priestess of the shrine, who had blessed him on his setting out, now came to welcome him back. He told her of the many dangers he had encountered and of how marvelously his life had been preserved through all—and she praised his courage and his warrior's prowess, and then putting on her most magnificent robes she returned thanks to their ancestress the Sun Goddess Amaterasu, to whose protection they both ascribed the Prince's wonderful preservation.

Here ends the story of Prince Yamato Take of Japan.

MOMOTARO, OR THE STORY OF THE SON OF A PEACH

Long, long ago there lived, an old man and an old woman; they were peasants, and had to work hard to earn their daily rice. The old man used to go and cut grass for the farmers around, and while he was gone the old woman, his wife, did the work of the house and worked in their own little rice field.

One day the old man went to the hills as usual to cut grass and the old woman took some clothes to the river to wash.

It was nearly summer, and the country was very beautiful to see in its fresh greenness as the two old people went on their way to work. The grass on the banks of the river looked like emerald velvet, and the pussy willows along the edge of the water were shaking out their soft tassels.

The breezes blew and ruffled the smooth surface of the water into wavelets, and passing on touched the cheeks of the old couple who, for some reason they could not explain, felt very happy that morning.

The old woman at last found a nice spot by the river bank and put her basket down. Then she set to work to wash the clothes; she took them one by one out of the basket and washed them in the river and rubbed them on the stones. The water was as clear as crystal, and she could see the tiny fish swimming to and fro, and the pebbles at the bottom.

As she was busy washing her clothes a great peach came bumping down the stream. The old woman looked up from her work and saw this large peach. She was sixty years of age, yet in all her life she had never seen such a big peach as this.

"How delicious that peach must be!" she said to herself. "I must certainly get it and take it home to my old man."

She stretched out her arm to try and get it, but it was quite out of her reach. She looked about for a stick, but there was not one to be seen, and if she went to look for one she would lose the peach.

Stopping a moment to think what she would do, she remembered an old charm-verse. Now she began to clap her hands to keep time to the rolling of the peach down stream, and while she clapped she sang this song:

> *"Distant water is bitter,*
> *The near water is sweet;*
> *Pass by the distant water*
> *And come into the sweet."*

Strange to say, as soon as she began to repeat this little song the peach began to come nearer and nearer the bank where the old woman was standing, till at last it stopped just in front of her so that she was able to take it up in her hands. The old woman was delighted. She could not go on with her work, so happy and excited was she, so she put all the clothes back in her bamboo basket, and with the basket on her back and the peach in her hand she hurried homewards.

It seemed a very long time to her to wait till her husband returned. The old man at last came back as the sun was setting, with a big bundle of grass on his back—so big that he was almost hidden and she could hardly see him. He seemed very tired and used the scythe for a walking stick, leaning on it as he walked along.

As soon as the old woman saw him she called out:

"O Fii San! (old man) I have been waiting for you to come home for such a long time to-day!"

"What is the matter? Why are you so impatient?" asked the old man, wondering at her unusual eagerness. "Has anything happened while I have been away?"

"Oh, no!" answered the old woman, "nothing has happened, only I have found a nice present for you!"

"That is good," said the old man. He then washed his feet in a basin of water and stepped up to the veranda.

The old woman now ran into the little room and brought out from the cupboard the big peach. It felt even heavier than before. She held it up to him, saying:

"Just look at this! Did you ever see such a large peach in all your life?"

When the old man looked at the peach he was greatly astonished and said:

"This is indeed the largest peach I have ever seen! Wherever did you buy it?"

"I did not buy it," answered the old woman. "I found it in the river where I was washing." And she told him the whole story.

"I am very glad that you have found it. Let us eat it now, for I am hungry," said the O Fii San.

He brought out the kitchen knife, and, placing the peach on a board, was about to cut it when, wonderful to tell, the peach split in two of itself and a clear voice said:

"Wait a bit, old man!" and out stepped a beautiful little child.

The old man and his wife were both so astonished at what they saw that they fell to the ground. The child spoke again:

"Don't be afraid. I am no demon or fairy. I will tell you the truth. Heaven has had compassion on you. Every day and every night you have lamented that you had no child. Your cry has been heard and I am sent to be the son of your old age!"

On hearing this the old man and his wife were very happy. They had cried night and day for sorrow at having no child to help them in their lonely old age, and now that their prayer was answered they were so lost with joy that they did not know where to put their hands or their feet. First the old man took the child up in his arms, and then the old woman did the same; and they named him MOMOTARO, OR SON OF A PEACH, because he had come out of a peach.

The years passed quickly by and the child grew to be fifteen years of age. He was taller and far stronger than any other boys of his own age, he had a handsome face and a heart full of courage, and he was very wise for his years. The old couple's pleasure was very great when they looked at him, for he was just what they thought a hero ought to be like.

One day Momotaro came to his foster-father and said solemnly:

"Father, by a strange chance we have become father and son. Your goodness to me has been higher than the mountain grasses which it was your daily work to cut, and deeper than the river where my mother washes the clothes. I do not know how to thank you enough."

"Why," answered the old man, "it is a matter of course that a father should bring up his son. When you are older it will be your turn to take care of us, so after all there will be no profit or loss between us—all will be equal. Indeed, I am rather surprised that you should thank me in this way!" and the old man looked bothered.

"I hope you will be patient with me," said Momotaro; "but before I begin to pay back your goodness to me I have a request to make which I hope you will grant me above everything else."

"I will let you do whatever you wish, for you are quite different to all other boys!"

"Then let me go away at once!"

"What do you say? Do you wish to leave your old father and mother and go away from your old home?"

"I will surely come back again, if you let me go now!"

"Where are you going?"

"You must think it strange that I want to go away," said Momotaro, "because I have not yet told you my reason. Far away from here to the northeast of Japan there is an island in the sea. This island is the stronghold of a band of devils. I have often heard how they invade this land, kill and rob the people, and carry off all they can find. They are not only very wicked but they are disloyal to our Emperor and disobey his laws. They are also cannibals, for they kill and eat some of the poor people who are so unfortunate as to fall into their hands. These devils are very hateful beings. I must go and conquer them and bring back all the plunder of which they have robbed this land. It is for this reason that I want to go away for a short time!"

The old man was much surprised at hearing all this from a mere boy of fifteen. He thought it best to let the boy go. He was strong and fearless, and besides all this, the old man knew he was no common child, for he had been sent to them as a gift from Heaven, and he felt quite sure that the devils would be powerless to harm him.

"All you say is very interesting, Momotaro," said the old man. "I will not hinder you in your determination. You may go if you wish. Go to the island as soon as ever you like and destroy the demons and bring peace to the land."

"Thank you, for all your kindness," said Momotaro, who began to get ready to go that very day. He was full of courage and did not know what fear was.

The old man and woman at once set to work to pound rice in the kitchen mortar to make cakes for Momotaro to take with him on his journey.

At last the cakes were made and Momotaro was ready to start on his long journey.

Parting is always sad. So it was now. The eyes of the two old people were filled with tears and their voices trembled as they said:

"Go with all care and speed. We expect you back victorious!"

Momotaro was very sorry to leave his old parents (though he knew he was coming back as soon as he could), for he thought of how lonely they would be while he was away. But he said "Good-by!" quite bravely.

"I am going now. Take good care of yourselves while I am away. Good-by!" And he stepped quickly out of the house. In silence the eyes of Momotaro and his parents met in farewell.

Momotaro now hurried on his way till it was midday. He began to feel hungry, so he opened his bag and took out one of the rice-cakes and sat down under a tree by the side of the road to eat it. While he was thus having his lunch a dog almost as large as a colt came running out from the high grass. He made straight for Momotaro, and showing his teeth, said in a fierce way:

"You are a rude man to pass my field without asking permission first. If you leave me all the cakes you have in your bag you may go; otherwise I will bite you till I kill you!"

Momotaro only laughed scornfully:

"What is that you are saying? Do you know who I am? I am Momotaro, and I am on my way to subdue the devils in their island stronghold in the northeast of Japan. If you try to stop me on my way there I will cut you in two from the head downwards!"

The dog's manner at once changed. His tail dropped between his legs, and coming near he bowed so low that his forehead touched the ground.

"What do I hear? The name of Momotaro? Are you indeed Momotaro? I have often heard of your great strength. Not knowing who you were I have behaved in a very stupid way. Will you please pardon my rudeness? Are you indeed on your way to invade the Island of Devils? If you will take such a rude fellow with you as one of your followers, I shall be very grateful to you."

"I think I can take you with me if you wish to go," said Momotaro.

"Thank you!" said the dog. "By the way, I am very very hungry. Will you give me one of the cakes you are carrying?"

"This is the best kind of cake there is in Japan," said Momotaro. "I cannot spare you a whole one; I will give you half of one."

"Thank you very much," said the dog, taking the piece thrown to him.

Then Momotaro got up and the dog followed. For a long time they walked over the hills and through the valleys. As they were going along an animal came down from a tree a little ahead of them. The creature soon came up to Momotaro and said:

"Good morning, Momotaro! You are welcome in this

part of the country. Will you allow me to go with you?"

The dog answered jealously:

"Momotaro already has a dog to accompany him. Of what use is a monkey like you in battle? We are on our way to fight the devils! Get away!"

The dog and the monkey began to quarrel and bite, for these two animals always hate each other.

"Now, don't quarrel!" said Momotaro, putting himself between them. "Wait a moment, dog!"

"It is not at all dignified for you to have such a creature as that following you!" said the dog.

"What do you know about it?" asked Momotaro; and pushing aside the dog, he spoke to the monkey:

"Who are you?"

"I am a monkey living in these hills," replied the monkey. "I heard of your expedition to the Island of Devils, and I have come to go with you. Nothing will please me more than to follow you!"

"Do you really wish to go to the Island of Devils and fight with me?"

"Yes, sir," replied the monkey.

"I admire your courage," said Momotaro. "Here is a piece of one of my fine rice-cakes. Come along!"

So the monkey joined Momotaro. The dog and the monkey did not get on well together. They were always snapping at each other as they went along, and always wanting to have a fight. This made Momotaro very cross, and at last he sent the dog on ahead with a flag and put the monkey behind with a sword, and he placed himself between them with a war-fan, which is made of iron.

By and by they came to a large field. Here a bird flew

down and alighted on the ground just in front of the little party. It was the most beautiful bird Momotaro had ever seen. On its body were five different robes of feathers and its head was covered with a scarlet cap.

The dog at once ran at the bird and tried to seize and kill it. But the bird struck out its spurs and flew at the dog's tail, and the fight went hard with both.

Momotaro, as he looked on, could not help admiring the bird; it showed so much spirit in the fight. It would certainly make a good fighter.

Momotaro went up to the two combatants, and holding the dog back, said to the bird:

"You rascal! you are hindering my journey. Surrender at once, and I will take you with me. If you don't I will set this dog to bite your head off!"

Then the bird surrendered at once, and begged to be taken into Momotaro's company.

"I do not know what excuse to offer for quarreling with the dog, your servant, but I did not see you. I am a miserable bird called a pheasant. It is very generous of you to pardon my rudeness and to take me with you. Please allow me to follow you behind the dog and the monkey!"

"I congratulate you on surrendering so soon," said Momotaro, smiling. "Come and join us in our raid on the devils."

"Are you going to take this bird with you also?" asked the dog, interrupting.

"Why do you ask such an unnecessary question? Didn't you hear what I said? I take the bird with me because I wish to!"

"Humph!" said the dog.

Then Momotaro stood and gave this order:

"Now all of you must listen to me. The first thing necessary in an army is harmony. It is a wise saying which says that 'Advantage on earth is better than advantage in Heaven!' Union amongst ourselves is better than any earthly gain. When we are not at peace amongst ourselves it is no easy thing to subdue an enemy. From now, you three, the dog, the monkey and the pheasant, must be friends with one mind. The one who first begins a quarrel will be discharged on the spot!"

All the three promised not to quarrel. The pheasant was now made a member of Momotaro's suite, and received half a cake.

Momotaro's influence was so great that the three became good friends, and hurried onwards with him as their leader.

Hurrying on day after day they at last came out upon the shore of the North-Eastern Sea. There was nothing to be seen as far as the horizon—not a sign of any island. All that broke the stillness was the rolling of the waves upon the shore.

Now, the dog and the monkey and the pheasant had come very bravely all the way through the long valleys and over the hills, but they had never seen the sea before, and for the first time since they set out they were bewildered and gazed at each other in silence. How were they to cross the water and get to the Island of Devils?

Momotaro soon saw that they were daunted by the sight of the sea, and to try them he spoke loudly and roughly:

"Why do you hesitate? Are you afraid of the sea? Oh! what cowards you are! It is impossible to take such weak creatures as you with me to fight the demons. It will be far better for me to go alone. I discharge you all at once!"

The three animals were taken aback at this sharp reproof, and clung to Momotaro's sleeve, begging him not to send them away.

"Please, Momotaro!" said the dog.

"We have come thus far!" said the monkey.

"It is inhuman to leave us here!" said the pheasant.

"We are not at all afraid of the sea," said the monkey again.

"Please do take us with you," said the pheasant.

"Do please," said the dog.

They had now gained a little courage, so Momotaro said:

"Well, then, I will take you with me, but be careful!"

Momotaro now got a small ship, and they all got on board. The wind and weather were fair, and the ship went like an arrow over the sea. It was the first time they had ever been on the water, and so at first the dog, the monkey and the pheasant were frightened at the waves and the rolling of the vessel, but by degrees they grew accustomed to the water and were quite happy again. Every day they paced the deck of their little ship, eagerly looking out for the demons' island.

When they grew tired of this, they told each other stories of all their exploits of which they were proud, and then played games together; and Momotaro found much to amuse him in listening to the three animals and watching their antics, and in this way he forgot that the way was long and that he was tired of the voyage and of doing nothing. He longed to be at work killing the monsters who had done so much harm in his country.

As the wind blew in their favor and they met no storms the ship made a quick voyage, and one day when the sun was shining brightly a sight of land rewarded the four watchers at the bow.

Momotaro knew at once that what they saw was the devils' stronghold. On the top of the precipitous shore, looking out to sea, was a large castle. Now that his enterprise was close at hand, he was deep in thought with his head leaning on his hands, wondering how he should begin the attack. His three followers watched him, waiting for orders. At last he called to the pheasant:

"It is a great advantage for us to have you with us." said Momotaro to the bird, "for you have good wings. Fly at once to the castle and engage the demons to fight. We will follow you."

The pheasant at once obeyed. He flew off from the ship beating the air gladly with his wings. The bird soon reached the island and took up his position on the roof in the middle of the castle, calling out loudly:

"All you devils listen to me! The great Japanese general Momotaro has come to fight you and to take your stronghold from you. If you wish to save your lives surrender at once, and in token of your submission you must break off the horns that grow on your forehead. If you do not surrender at once, but make up your mind to fight, we, the pheasant, the dog and the monkey, will kill you all by biting and tearing you to death!"

The horned demons looking up and only seeing a pheasant, laughed and said:

"A wild pheasant, indeed! It is ridiculous to hear such words from a mean thing like you. Wait till you get a blow from one of our iron bars!"

Very angry, indeed, were the devils. They shook their horns and their shocks of red hair fiercely, and rushed to put on tiger skin trousers to make themselves look more terrible. They then brought out great iron bars and ran to where the pheasant perched over their heads, and tried to knock him down. The pheasant flew to one side to escape the blow, and then attacked the head of first one and then another demon. He flew round and round them, beating the air with his wings so fiercely and ceaselessly, that the devils began to wonder whether they had to fight one or many more birds.

In the meantime, Momotaro had brought his ship to land. As they had approached, he saw that the shore was like a precipice, and that the large castle was surrounded by high walls and large iron gates and was strongly fortified.

Momotaro landed, and with the hope of finding some way of entrance, walked up the path towards the top, followed by the monkey and the dog. They soon came upon two beautiful damsels washing clothes in a stream. Momotaro saw that the clothes were blood-stained, and that as the two maidens washed, the tears were falling fast down their cheeks. He stopped and spoke to them:

"Who are you, and why do you weep?"

"We are captives of the Demon King. We were carried away from our homes to this island, and though we are the daughters of Daimios (Lords), we are obliged to be his servants, and one day he will kill us"—and the maidens held up the blood-stained clothes—"and eat us, and there is no one to help us!"

And their tears burst out afresh at this horrible thought.

"I will rescue you," said Momotaro. "Do not weep any more, only show me how I may get into the castle."

Then the two ladies led the way and showed Momotaro a little back door in the lowest part of the castle wall—so small that Momotaro could hardly crawl in.

The pheasant, who was all this time fighting hard, saw Momotaro and his little band rush in at the back.

Momotaro's onslaught was so furious that the devils

could not stand against him. At first their foe had been a single bird, the pheasant, but now that Momotaro and the dog and the monkey had arrived they were bewildered, for the four enemies fought like a hundred, so strong were they. Some of the devils fell off the parapet of the castle and were dashed to pieces on the rocks beneath; others fell into the sea and were drowned; many were beaten to death by the three animals.

The chief of the devils at last was the only one left. He made up his mind to surrender, for he knew that his enemy was stronger than mortal man.

He came up humbly to Momotaro and threw down his iron bar, and kneeling down at the victor's feet he broke off the horns on his head in token of submission, for they were the sign of his strength and power.

"I am afraid of you," he said meekly. "I cannot stand against you. I will give you all the treasure hidden in this castle if you will spare my life!"

Momotaro laughed.

"It is not like you, big devil, to beg for mercy, is it? I cannot spare your wicked life, however much you beg, for you have killed and tortured many people and robbed our country for many years."

Then Momotaro tied the devil chief up and gave him into the monkey's charge. Having done this, he went into all the rooms of the castle and set the prisoners free and gathered together all the treasure he found.

The dog and the pheasant carried home the plunder, and thus Momotaro returned triumphantly to his home, taking with him the devil chief as a captive.

The two poor damsels, daughters of Daimios, and others whom the wicked demon had carried off to be his slaves, were taken safely to their own homes and delivered to their parents.

The whole country made a hero of Momotaro on his triumphant return, and rejoiced that the country was now freed from the robber devils who had been a terror of the land for a long time.

The old couple's joy was greater than ever, and the treasure Momotaro had brought home with him enabled them to live in peace and plenty to the end of their days.

THE OGRE OF RASHOMON

Long, long ago in Kyoto, the people of the city were terrified by accounts of a dreadful ogre, who, it was said, haunted the Gate of Rashomon at twilight and seized whoever passed by. The missing victims were never seen again, so it was whispered that the ogre was a horrible cannibal, who not only killed the unhappy victims but ate them also. Now everybody in the town and neighborhood was in great fear, and no one durst venture out after sunset near the Gate of Rashomon.

Now at this time there lived in Kyoto a general named Raiko, who had made himself famous for his brave deeds. Some time before this he made the country ring with his name, for he had attacked Oeyama, where a band of ogres lived with their chief, who instead of wine drank the blood of human beings. He had routed them all and cut off the head of the chief monster.

This brave warrior was always followed by a band of faithful knights. In this band there were five knights of great valor. One evening as the five knights sat at a feast quaffing SAKE in their rice bowls and eating all kinds of fish, raw, and stewed, and broiled, and toasting each other's healths and exploits, the first knight, Hojo, said to the others:

"Have you all heard the rumor that every evening after sunset there comes an ogre to the Gate of Rashomon, and that he seizes all who pass by?"

The second knight, Watanabe, answered him, saying:

"Do not talk such nonsense! All the ogres were killed by our chief Raiko at Oeyama! It cannot be true, because even if any ogres did escape from that great killing they would not dare to show themselves in this city, for they know that our brave master would at once attack them if he knew that any of them were still alive!"

"Then do you disbelieve what I say, and think that I am telling you a falsehood?"

"No, I do not think that you are telling a lie," said Watanabe; "but you have heard some old woman's story which is not worth believing."

"Then the best plan is to prove what I say, by going there yourself and finding out yourself whether it is true or not," said Hojo.

Watanabe, the second knight, could not bear the thought that his companion should believe he was afraid, so he answered quickly:

"Of course, I will go at once and find out for myself!"

So Watanabe at once got ready to go—he buckled on his long sword and put on a coat of armor, and tied on his large helmet. When he was ready to start he said to the others:

"Give me something so that I can prove I have been there!"

Then one of the men got a roll of writing paper and his box of Indian ink and brushes, and the four comrades wrote their names on a piece of paper.

"I will take this," said Watanabe, "and put it on the Gate of Rashomon, so to-morrow morning will you all go and look at it? I may be able to catch an ogre or two by then!" and he mounted his horse and rode off gallantly.

It was a very dark night, and there was neither moon nor star to light Watanabe on his way. To make the darkness worse a storm came on, the rain fell heavily and the wind howled like wolves in the mountains. Any ordinary man would have trembled at the thought of going out of doors, but

Watanabe was a brave warrior and dauntless, and his honor and word were at stake, so he sped on into the night, while his companions listened to the sound of his horse's hoofs dying away in the distance, then shut the sliding shutters close and gathered round the charcoal fire and wondered what would happen—and whether their comrade would encounter one of those horrible Oni.

At last Watanabe reached the Gate of Rashomon, but peer as he might through the darkness he could see no sign of an ogre.

"It is just as I thought," said Watanabe to himself; "there are certainly no ogres here; it is only an old woman's story. I will stick this paper on the gate so that the others can see I have been here when they come to-morrow, and then I will take my way home and laugh at them all."

He fastened the piece of paper, signed by all his four companions, on the gate, and then turned his horse's head towards home.

As he did so he became aware that some one was behind him, and at the same time a voice called out to him to wait. Then his helmet was seized from the back. "Who are you?" said Watanabe fearlessly. He then put out his hand and groped around to find out who or what it was that held him by the helmet. As he did so he touched something that felt like an arm—it was covered with hair and as big round as the trunk of a tree!

Watanabe knew at once that this was the arm of an ogre, so he drew his sword and cut at it fiercely.

There was a loud yell of pain, and then the ogre dashed in front of the warrior.

Watanabe's eyes grew large with wonder, for he saw that

the ogre was taller than the great gate, his eyes were flashing like mirrors in the sunlight, and his huge mouth was wide open, and as the monster breathed, flames of fire shot out of his mouth.

The ogre thought to terrify his foe, but Watanabe never flinched. He attacked the ogre with all his strength, and thus they fought face to face for a long time. At last the ogre, finding that he could neither frighten nor beat Watanabe and that he might himself be beaten, took to flight. But Watanabe, determined not to let the monster escape, put spurs to his horse and gave chase.

But though the knight rode very fast the ogre ran faster, and to his disappointment he found himself unable to overtake the monster, who was gradually lost to sight.

Watanabe returned to the gate where the fierce fight had taken place, and got down from his horse. As he did so he stumbled upon something lying on the ground.

Stooping to pick it up he found that it was one of the ogre's huge arms which he must have slashed off in the fight. His joy was great at having secured such a prize, for this was the best of all proofs of his adventure with the ogre. So he took it up carefully and carried it home as a trophy of his victory.

When he got back, he showed the arm to his comrades, who one and all called him the hero of their band and gave him a great feast. His wonderful deed was soon noised abroad in Kyoto, and people from far and near came to see the ogre's arm.

Watanabe now began to grow uneasy as to how he should keep the arm in safety, for he knew that the ogre to whom it belonged was still alive. He felt sure that one day or other, as soon as the ogre got over his scare, he would come to try to get his arm back again. Watanabe therefore had a box made of the strongest wood and banded with iron. In this he placed the arm, and then he sealed down the heavy lid, refusing to open it for anyone. He kept the box in his own room and took charge of it himself, never allowing it out of his sight.

Now one night he heard some one knocking at the porch, asking for admittance.

When the servant went to the door to see who it was, there was only an old woman, very respectable in appearance. On being asked who she was and what was her business, the old woman replied with a smile that she had been nurse to the master of the house when he was a little baby. If the lord of the house were at home she begged to be allowed to see him.

The servant left the old woman at the door and went to tell his master that his old nurse had come to see him. Watanabe thought it strange that she should come at that time of night, but at the thought of his old nurse, who had been like a foster-mother to him and whom he had not seen for a long time, a very tender feeling sprang up for her in his heart. He ordered the servant to show her in.

The old woman was ushered into the room, and after the customary bows and greetings were over, she said:

"Master, the report of your brave fight with the ogre at the Gate of Rashomon is so widely known that even your poor old nurse has heard of it. Is it really true, what every one says, that you cut off one of the ogre's arms? If you did, your deed is highly to be praised!"

"I was very disappointed," said Watanabe, "that I was not able take the monster captive, which was what I wished to do, instead of only cutting off an arm!"

"I am very proud to think," answered the old woman,

"that my master was so brave as to dare to cut off an ogre's arm. There is nothing that can be compared to your courage. Before I die it is the great wish of my life to see this arm," she added pleadingly.

"No," said Watanabe, "I am sorry, but I cannot grant your request."

"But why?" asked the old woman.

"Because," replied Watanabe, "ogres are very revengeful creatures, and if I open the box there is no telling but that the ogre may suddenly appear and carry off his arm. I have had a box made on purpose with a very strong lid, and in this box I keep the ogre's arm secure; and I never show it to any one, whatever happens."

"Your precaution is very reasonable," said the old woman. "But I am your old nurse, so surely you will not refuse to show ME the arm. I have only just heard of your brave act, and not being able to wait till the morning I came at once to ask you to show it to me."

Watanabe was very troubled at the old woman's pleading, but he still persisted in refusing. Then the old woman said:

"Do you suspect me of being a spy sent by the ogre?"

"No, of course I do not suspect you of being the ogre's spy, for you are my old nurse," answered Watanabe.

"Then you cannot surely refuse to show me the arm any longer." entreated the old woman; "for it is the great wish of my heart to see for once in my life the arm of an ogre!"

Watanabe could not hold out in his refusal any longer, so he gave in at last, saying:

"Then I will show you the ogre's arm, since you so earnestly wish to see it. Come, follow me!" and he led the way to his own room, the old woman following.

When they were both in the room Watanabe shut the door carefully, and then going towards a big box which stood in a corner of the room, he took off the heavy lid. He then called to the old woman to come near and look in, for he never took the arm out of the box.

"What is it like? Let me have a good look at it," said the old nurse, with a joyful face.

She came nearer and nearer, as if she were afraid, till she stood right against the box. Suddenly she plunged her hand into the box and seized the arm, crying with a fearful voice which made the room shake:

"Oh, joy! I have got my arm back again!"

And from an old woman she was suddenly transformed into the towering figure of the frightful ogre!

Watanabe sprang back and was unable to move for a moment, so great was his astonishment; but recognizing the ogre who had attacked him at the Gate of Rashomon, he determined with his usual courage to put an end to him this time. He seized his sword, drew it out of its sheath in a flash, and tried to cut the ogre down.

So quick was Watanabe that the creature had a narrow escape. But the ogre sprang up to the ceiling, and bursting through the roof, disappeared in the mist and clouds.

In this way the ogre escaped with his arm. The knight gnashed his teeth with disappointment, but that was all he could do. He waited in patience for another opportunity to dispatch the ogre. But the latter was afraid of Watanabe's great strength and daring, and never troubled Kyoto again. So once more the people of the city were able to go out without fear even at night time, and the brave deeds of Watanabe have never been forgotten!

HOW AN OLD MAN LOST HIS WEN

Many, many years ago there lived a good old man who had a wen like a tennis-ball growing out of his right cheek. This lump was a great disfigurement to the old man, and so annoyed him that for many years he spent all his time and money in trying to get rid of it. He tried everything he could think of. He consulted many doctors far and near, and took all kinds of medicines both internally and externally. But it was all of no use. The lump only grew bigger and bigger till it was nearly as big as his face, and in despair he gave up all hopes of ever losing it, and resigned himself to the thought of having to carry the lump on his face all his life.

One day the firewood gave out in his kitchen, so, as his wife wanted some at once, the old man took his ax and set out for the woods up among the hills not very far from his home. It was a fine day in the early autumn, and the old man enjoyed the fresh air and was in no hurry to get home. So the whole afternoon passed quickly while he was chopping wood, and he had collected a goodly pile to take back to his wife. When the day began to draw to a close, he turned his face homewards.

The old man had not gone far on his way down the mountain pass when the sky clouded and rain began to fall heavily. He looked about for some shelter, but there was not even a charcoal-burner's hut near. At last he espied a large hole in the hollow trunk of a tree. The hole was near the ground, so he crept in easily, and sat down in hopes that he had only been overtaken by a mountain shower, and that the weather would soon clear.

But much to the old man's disappointment, instead of

clearing the rain fell more and more heavily, and finally a heavy thunderstorm broke over the mountain. The thunder roared so terrifically, and the heavens seemed to be so ablaze with lightning, that the old man could hardly believe himself to be alive. He thought that he must die of fright. At last, however, the sky cleared, and the whole country was aglow in the rays of the setting sun. The old man's spirits revived when he looked out at the beautiful twilight, and he was about to step out from his strange hiding-place in the hollow tree when the sound of what seemed like the approaching steps of several people caught his ear. He at once thought that his friends had come to look for him, and he was delighted at the idea of having some jolly companions with whom to walk home. But on looking out from the tree, what was his amazement to see, not his friends, but hundreds of demons coming towards the spot. The more he looked, the greater was his astonishment. Some of these demons were as large as giants, others had great big eyes out of all proportion to the rest of their bodies, others again had absurdly long noses, and some had such big mouths that they seemed to open from ear to ear. All had horns growing on their foreheads. The old man was so surprised at what he saw that he lost his balance and fell out of the hollow tree. Fortunately for him the demons did not see him, as the tree was in the background. So he picked himself up and crept back into the tree.

While he was sitting there and wondering impatiently when he would be able to get home, he heard the sounds of gay music, and then some of the demons began to sing.

"What are these creatures doing?" said the old man to himself. "I will look out, it sounds very amusing."

On peeping out, the old man saw that the demon chief

himself was actually sitting with his back against the tree in which he had taken refuge, and all the other demons were sitting round, some drinking and some dancing. Food and wine was spread before them on the ground, and the demons were evidently having a great entertainment and enjoying themselves immensely.

It made the old man laugh to see their strange antics.

"How amusing this is!" laughed the old man to himself "I am now quite old, but I have never seen anything so strange in all my life."

He was so interested and excited in watching all that the demons were doing, that he forgot himself and stepped out of the tree and stood looking on.

The demon chief was just taking a big cup of SAKE and watching one of the demons dancing. In a little while he said with a bored air:

"Your dance is rather monotonous. I am tired of watching it. Isn't there any one amongst you all who can dance better than this fellow?"

Now the old man had been fond of dancing all his life, and was quite an expert in the art, and he knew that he could do much better than the demon.

"Shall I go and dance before these demons and let them see what a human being can do? It may be dangerous, for if I don't please them they may kill me!" said the old fellow to himself.

His fears, however, were soon overcome by his love of dancing. In a few minutes he could restrain himself no longer, and came out before the whole party of demons and began to dance at once. The old man, realizing that his life probably depended on whether he pleased these strange creatures or not, exerted his skill and wit to the utmost.

The demons were at first very surprised to see a man so fearlessly taking part in their entertainment, and then their surprise soon gave place to admiration.

"How strange!" exclaimed the horned chief. "I never saw such a skillful dancer before! He dances admirably!"

When the old man had finished his dance, the big demon said:

"Thank you very much for your amusing dance. Now give us the pleasure of drinking a cup of wine with us," and with these words he handed him his largest wine-cup.

The old man thanked him very humbly:

"I did not expect such kindness from your lordship. I fear I have only disturbed your pleasant party by my unskillful dancing."

"No, no," answered the big demon. "You must come often and dance for us. Your skill has given us much pleasure."

The old man thanked him again and promised to do so.

"Then will you come again to-morrow, old man?" asked the demon.

"Certainly, I will," answered the old man.

"Then you must leave some pledge of your word with us," said the demon.

"Whatever you like," said the old man.

"Now what is the best thing he can leave with us as a pledge?" asked the demon, looking round.

Then said one of the demon's attendants kneeling behind the chief:

"The token he leaves with us must be the most important thing to him in his possession. I see the old man has a wen on his right cheek. Now mortal men consider such a wen very fortunate. Let my lord take the lump from the old man's right cheek, and he will surely come to-morrow, if only to get that back."

"You are very clever," said the demon chief, giving his horns an approving nod. Then he stretched out a hairy arm and claw-like hand, and took the great lump from the old man's right cheek. Strange to say, it came off as easily as a ripe plum from the tree at the demon's touch, and then the merry troop of demons suddenly vanished.

The old man was lost in bewilderment by all that had happened. He hardly knew for some time where he was. When he came to understand what had happened to him, he was delighted to find that the lump on his face, which had for so many years disfigured him, had really been taken away without any pain to himself. He put up his hand to feel if any scar remained, but found that his right cheek was as smooth as his left.

The sun had long set, and the young moon had risen like a silver crescent in the sky. The old man suddenly realized how late it was and began to hurry home. He patted his right cheek all the time, as if to make sure of his good fortune in having lost the wen. He was so happy that he found it impossible to walk quietly—he ran and danced the whole way home.

He found his wife very anxious, wondering what had happened to make him so late. He soon told her all that had passed since he left home that afternoon. She was quite as happy as her husband when he showed her that the ugly lump had disappeared from his face, for in her youth she had prided herself on his good looks, and it had been a daily grief to her to see the horrid growth.

Now next door to this good old couple there lived a wicked and disagreeable old man. He, too, had for many years been troubled with the growth of a wen on his left cheek, and he, too, had tried all manner of things to get rid of it, but in vain.

He heard at once, through the servant, of his neighbor's good luck in losing the lump on his face, so he called that very evening and asked his friend to tell him everything that concerned the loss of it. The good old man told his disagreeable neighbor all that had happened to him. He described the place where he would find the hollow tree in which to hide, and advised him to be on the spot in the late afternoon towards the time of sunset.

The old neighbor started out the very next afternoon, and after hunting about for some time, came to the hollow tree just as his friend had described. Here he hid himself and waited for the twilight.

Just as he had been told, the band of demons came at that hour and held a feast with dance and song. When this had gone on for some time the chief of the demons looked around and said:

"It is now time for the old man to come as he promised us. Why doesn't he come?"

When the second old man heard these words he ran out of his hiding-place in the tree and, kneeling down before the Oni, said:

"I have been waiting for a long time for you to speak!"

"Ah, you are the old man of yesterday," said the demon chief. "Thank you for coming, you must dance for us soon."

The old man now stood up and opened his fan and began to dance. But he had never learned to dance, and knew nothing about the necessary gestures and different positions.

He thought that anything would please the demons, so he just hopped about, waving his arms and stamping his feet, imitating as well as he could any dancing he had ever seen.

The Oni were very dissatisfied at this exhibition, and said amongst themselves:

"How badly he dances to-day!"

Then to the old man the demon chief said:

"Your performance to-day is quite different from the dance of yesterday. We don't wish to see any more of such dancing. We will give you back the pledge you left with us. You must go away at once."

With these words he took out from a fold of his dress the lump which he had taken from the face of the old man who had danced so well the day before, and threw it at the right cheek of the old man who stood before him. The lump immediately attached itself to his cheek as firmly as if it had grown there always, and all attempts to pull it off were useless. The wicked old man, instead of losing the lump on his left cheek as he had hoped, found to his dismay that he had but added another to his right cheek in his attempt to get rid of the first.

He put up first one hand and then the other to each side of his face to make sure if he were not dreaming a horrible nightmare. No, sure enough there was now a great wen on the right side of his face as on the left. The demons had all disappeared, and there was nothing for him to do but to return home. He was a pitiful sight, for his face, with the two large lumps, one on each side, looked just like a Japanese gourd.

GREEN WILLOW

Tomodata, the young *samurai*, owed allegiance to the Lord of Noto. He was a soldier, a courtier, and a poet. He had a sweet voice and a beautiful face, a noble form and a very winning address. He was a graceful dancer, and excelled in every manly sport. He was wealthy and generous and kind. He was beloved by rich and by poor.

Now his *daimyo*, the Lord of Noto, wanted a man to undertake a mission of trust. He chose Tomodata, and called him to his presence.

"Are you loyal?" said the *daimyo*.

"My lord, you know it," answered Tomodata.

"Do you love me, then?" asked the *daimyo*.

"Ay, my good lord," said Tomodata, kneeling before him.

"Then carry my message," said the *daimyo*. "Ride and do not spare your beast. Ride straight, and fear not the mountains nor the enemies' country. Stay not for storm nor any other thing. Lose your life; but betray not your trust. Above all, do not look any maid between the eyes. Ride, and bring me word again quickly."

Thus spoke the Lord of Noto.

So Tomodata got him to horse, and away he rode upon his quest. Obedient to his lord's commands, he spared not his good beast. He rode straight, and was not afraid of the steep mountain passes nor of the enemies' country. Ere he had been three days upon the road the autumn tempest burst, for it was the ninth month. Down poured the rain in a torrent. Tomodata bowed his head and rode on. The wind howled in the pine-tree branches. It blew a typhoon. The good horse trembled and could scarcely keep its feet, but Tomodata spoke to it and urged it on. His own cloak he drew close about him and held it so that it might not blow away, and in this wise he rode on.

The fierce storm swept away many a familiar landmark of the road, and buffeted the *samurai* so that he became weary almost to fainting. Noontide was as dark as twilight, twilight was as dark as night, and when night fell it was as black as the night of Yomi, where lost souls wander and cry. By this time Tomodata had lost his way in a wild, lonely place, where, as it seemed to him, no human soul inhabited. His horse could carry him no longer, and he wandered on foot through bogs and marshes, through rocky and thorny tracks, until he fell into deep despair.

"Alack!" he cried, "must I die in this wilderness and the quest of the Lord of Noto be unfulfilled?"

At this moment the great winds blew away the clouds of the sky, so that the moon shone very brightly forth, and by the sudden light Tomodata saw a little hill on his right hand. Upon the hill was a small thatched cottage, and before the cottage grew three green weeping-willow trees.

"Now, indeed, the gods be thanked!" said Tomodata, and he climbed the hill in no time. Light shone from the chinks of the cottage door, and smoke curled out of a hole in the roof. The three willow trees swayed and flung out their green streamers in the wind. Tomodata threw his horse's rein over a branch of one of them, and called for admittance to the longed-for shelter.

At once the cottage door was opened by an old woman, very poorly but neatly clad.

"Who rides abroad upon such a night?" she asked, "and what wills he here?"

"I am a weary traveller, lost and benighted upon your

lonely moor. My name is Tomodata. I am a *samurai* in the service of the Lord of Noto, upon whose business I ride. Show me hospitality for the love of the gods. I crave food and shelter for myself and my horse."

As the young man stood speaking the water streamed from his garments. He reeled a little, and put out a hand to hold on by the side-post of the door.

"Come in, come in, young sir!" cried the old woman, full of pity. "Come in to the warm fire. You are very welcome. We have but coarse fare to offer, but it shall be set before you with great good-will. As to your horse, I see you have delivered him to my daughter; he is in good hands."

At this Tomodata turned sharply round. Just behind him, in the dim light, stood a very young girl with the horse's rein thrown over her arm. Her garments were blown about and her long loose hair streamed out upon the wind. The *samurai* wondered how she had come there. Then the old woman drew him into the cottage and shut the door. Before the fire sat the good man of the house, and the two old people did the very best they could for Tomodata. They gave him dry garments, comforted him with hot rice wine, and quickly prepared a good supper for him.

Presently the daughter of the house came in, and retired behind a screen to comb her hair and to dress afresh. Then she came forth to wait upon him. She wore a blue robe of homespun cotton. Her feet were bare. Her hair was not tied nor confined in any way, but lay along her smooth cheeks, and hung, straight and long and black, to her very knees. She was slender and graceful. Tomodata judged her to be about fifteen years old, and knew well that she was the fairest maiden he had ever seen.

At length she knelt at his side to pour wine into his cup. She held the wine-bottle in two hands and bent her head. Tomodata turned to look at her. When she had made an end of pouring the wine and had set down the bottle, their glances met, and Tomodata looked at her full between the eyes, for he forgot altogether the warning of his *daimyo*, the Lord of Noto.

"Maiden," he said, "what is your name?"

She answered: "They call me the Green Willow."

"The dearest name on earth," he said, and again he looked her between the eyes. And because he looked so long her face grew rosy red, from chin to forehead, and though she smiled her eyes filled with tears.

Ah me, for the Lord of Noto's quest!

Then Tomodata made this little song:

> *"Long-haired maiden, do you know*
> *That with the red dawn I must go?*
> *Do you wish me far away?*
> *Cruel long-haired maiden, say—*
> *Long-haired maiden, if you know*
> *That with the red dawn I must go,*
> *Why, oh why, do you blush so?"*

And the maiden, the Green Willow, answered:

> *"The dawn comes if I will or no;*
> *Never leave me, never go.*
> *My sleeve shall hide the blush away.*
> *The dawn comes if I will or no;*
> *Never leave me, never go.*
> *Lord, I lift my long sleeve so...."*

"Oh, Green Willow, Green Willow..." sighed Tomodata.

That night he lay before the fire—still, but with wide eyes, for no sleep came to him though he was weary. He was sick for love of the Green Willow. Yet by the rules of his service he was bound in honour to think of no such thing. Moreover, he had the quest of the Lord of Noto that lay heavy on his heart, and he longed to keep truth and loyalty.

At the first peep of day he rose up. He looked upon the kind old man who had been his host, and left a purse of gold at his side as he slept. The maiden and her mother lay behind the screen.

Tomodata saddled and bridled his horse, and mounting, rode slowly away through the mist of the early morning. The storm was quite over and it was as still as Paradise. The green grass and the leaves shone with the wet. The sky was clear, and the path very bright with autumn flowers; but Tomodata was sad.

When the sunlight streamed across his saddlebow, "Ah, Green Willow, Green Willow," he sighed; and at noontide it was "Green Willow, Green Willow"; and "Green Willow, Green Willow," when the twilight fell. That night he lay in a deserted shrine, and the place was so holy that in spite of all he slept from midnight till the dawn. Then he rose, having it in his mind to wash himself in a cold stream that flowed near by, so as to go refreshed upon his journey; but he was stopped upon the shrine's threshold. There lay the Green Willow, prone upon the ground. A slender thing she lay, face downwards, with her black hair flung about her. She lifted a hand and held Tomodata by the sleeve. "My lord, my lord," she said, and fell to sobbing piteously.

He took her in his arms without a word, and soon he set her on his horse before him, and together they rode the live-long day. It was little they recked of the road they went, for all the while they looked into each other's eyes. The heat and the cold were nothing to them. They felt not the sun nor the rain; of truth or falsehood they thought nothing at all; nor of filial piety, nor of the Lord of Noto's quest, nor of honour nor plighted word. They knew but the one thing. Alas, for the ways of love!

At last they came to an unknown city, where they stayed. Tomodata carried gold and jewels in his girdle, so they found a house built of white wood, spread with sweet white mats. In every dim room there could be heard the sound of the garden waterfall, whilst the swallow flitted across and across the paper lattice. Here they dwelt, knowing but the one thing. Here they dwelt three years of happy days, and for Tomodata and the Green Willow the years were like garlands of sweet flowers.

In the autumn of the third year it chanced that the two of them went forth into the garden at dusk, for they had a wish to see the round moon rise; and as they watched, the Green Willow began to shake and shiver.

"My dear," said Tomodata, "you shake and shiver; and it is no wonder, the night wind is chill. Come in." And he put his arm around her.

At this she gave a long and pitiful cry, very loud and full of agony, and when she had uttered the cry she failed, and dropped her head upon her love's breast.

"Tomodata," she whispered, "say a prayer for me; I die."

"Oh, say not so, my sweet, my sweet! You are but weary; you are faint."

He carried her to the stream's side, where the iris grew like swords, and the lotus-leaves like shields, and laved her forehead with water. He said: "What is it, my dear? Look up and live."

"The tree," she moaned, "the tree ... they have cut down my tree. Remember the Green Willow."

With that she slipped, as it seemed, from his arms to his feet; and he, casting himself upon the ground, found only silken garments, bright coloured, warm and sweet, and straw sandals, scarlet-thonged.

In after years, when Tomodata was a holy man, he travelled from shrine to shrine, painfully upon his feet, and acquired much merit.

Once, at nightfall, he found himself upon a lonely moor. On his right hand he beheld a little hill, and on it the sad ruins of a poor thatched cottage. The door swung to and fro with broken latch and creaking hinge. Before it stood three old stumps of willow trees that had long since been cut down. Tomodata stood for a long time still and silent. Then he sang gently to himself:

> *"Long-haired maiden, do you know*
> *That with the red dawn I must go?*
> *Do you wish me far away?*
> *Cruel long-haired maiden, say—*
> *Long-haired maiden, if you know*
> *That with the red dawn I must go,*
> *Why, oh why, do you blush so?"*

"Ah, foolish song! The gods forgive me.... I should have recited the Holy Sutra for the Dead," said Tomodata.

THE FLUTE

Long since, there lived in Yedo a gentleman of good lineage and very honest conversation. His wife was a gentle and loving lady. To his secret grief, she bore him no sons. But a daughter she did give him, whom they called O'Yoné, which, being interpreted, is "Rice in the ear." Each of them loved this child more than life, and guarded her as the apple of their eye. And the child grew up red and white, and long-eyed, straight and slender as the green bamboo.

When O'Yoné was twelve years old, her mother drooped with the fall of the year, sickened, and pined, and ere the red had faded from the leaves of the maples she was dead and shrouded and laid in the earth. The husband was wild in his grief. He cried aloud, he beat his breast, he lay upon the ground and refused comfort, and for days he neither broke his fast nor slept. The child was quite silent.

Time passed by. The man perforce went about his business. The snows of winter fell and covered his wife's grave. The beaten pathway from his house to the dwelling of the dead was snow also, undisturbed save for the faint prints of a child's sandalled feet. In the spring-time he girded up his robe and went forth to see the cherry blossom, making merry enough, and writing a poem upon gilded paper, which he hung to a cherry-tree branch to flutter in the wind. The poem was in praise of the spring and of *saké*. Later, he planted the orange lily of forgetfulness, and thought of his wife no more. But the child remembered.

Before the year was out he brought a new bride home, a woman with a fair face and a black heart. But the man, poor fool, was happy, and commended his child to her, and believed that all was well.

Now because her father loved O'Yoné, her stepmother hated her with a jealous and deadly hatred, and every day she dealt cruelly by the child, whose gentle ways and patience only angered her the more. But because of her father's presence she did not dare to do O'Yoné any great ill; therefore she waited, biding her time. The poor child passed her days and her nights in torment and horrible fear. But of these things she said not a word to her father. Such is the manner of children.

Now, after some time, it chanced that the man was called away by his business to a distant city. Kioto was the name of the city, and from Yedo it is many days' journey on foot or on horseback. Howbeit, go the man needs must, and stay there three moons or more. Therefore he made ready, and equipped himself, and his servants that were to go with him, with all things needful; and so came to the last night before his departure, which was to be very early in the morning.

He called O'Yoné to him and said: "Come here, then, my dear little daughter." So O'Yoné went and knelt before him.

"What gift shall I bring you home from Kioto?" he said.

But she hung her head and did not answer.

"Answer, then, rude little one," he bade her. "Shall it be a golden fan, or a roll of silk, or a new *obi* of red brocade, or a great battledore with images upon it and many light-feathered shuttlecocks?"

Then she burst into bitter weeping, and he took her upon his knees to soothe her. But she hid her face with her sleeves and cried as if her heart would break. And, "O father, father, father," she said, "do not go away—do not go away!"

"But, my sweet, I needs must," he answered, "and soon I shall be back—so soon, scarcely it will seem that I am gone, when I shall be here again with fair gifts in my hand."

"Father, take me with you," she said.

"Alas, what a great way for a little girl! Will you walk on your feet, my little pilgrim, or mount a pack-horse? And how would you fare in the inns of Kioto? Nay, my dear, stay; it is but for a little time, and your kind mother will be with you."

She shuddered in his arms.

"Father, if you go, you will never see me more."

Then the father felt a sudden chill about his heart, that gave him pause. But he would not heed it. What! Must he, a strong man grown, be swayed by a child's fancies? He put O'Yoné gently from him, and she slipped away as silently as a shadow.

But in the morning she came to him before sunrise with a little flute in her hand, fashioned of bamboo and smoothly polished. "I made it myself," she said, "from a bamboo in the grove that is behind our garden. I made it for you. As you cannot take me with you, take the little flute, honourable father. Play on it sometimes, if you will, and think of me." Then she wrapped it in a handkerchief of white silk, lined with scarlet, and wound a scarlet cord about it, and gave it to her father, who put it in his sleeve. After this he departed and went his way, taking the road to Kioto. As he went he looked back thrice, and beheld his child, standing at the gate, looking after him. Then the road turned and he saw her no more.

The city of Kioto was passing great and beautiful, and so the father of O'Yoné found it. And what with his business during the day, which sped very well, and his pleasure in the evening, and his sound sleep at night, the time passed merrily, and small thought he gave to Yedo, to his home, or to his child. Two moons passed, and three, and he made no plans for return.

One evening he was making ready to go forth to a great supper of his friends, and as he searched in his chest for certain brave silken *hakama* which he intended to wear as an honour to the feast, he came upon the little flute, which had lain hidden all this time in the sleeve of his travelling dress. He drew it forth from its red and white handkerchief, and as he did so, felt strangely cold with an icy chill that crept about his heart. He hung over the live charcoal of the *hibachi* as one in a dream. He put the flute to his lips, when there came from it a long-drawn wail.

He dropped it hastily upon the mats and clapped his hands for his servant, and told him he would not go forth that night. He was not well, he would be alone. After a long time he reached out his hand for the flute. Again that long, melancholy cry. He shook from head to foot, but he blew into the flute. "Come back to Yedo ... come back to Yedo.... Father! Father!" The quavering childish voice rose to a shriek and then broke.

A horrible foreboding now took possession of the man, and he was as one beside himself. He flung himself from the house and from the city, and journeyed day and night, denying himself sleep and food. So pale was he and wild that the people deemed him a madman and fled from him, or pitied him as the afflicted of the gods. At last he came to his journey's end, travel-stained from head to heel, with bleeding feet and half-dead of weariness.

His wife met him in the gate.

He said: "Where is the child?"

"The child...?" she answered.

"Ay, the child—my child ... where is she?" he cried in an agony.

The woman laughed: "Nay, my lord, how should I know? She is within at her books, or she is in the garden, or she is asleep, or mayhap she has gone forth with her playmates, or ..."

He said: "Enough; no more of this. Come, where is my child?"

Then she was afraid. And, "In the Bamboo Grove," she said, looking at him with wide eyes.

There the man ran, and sought O'Yoné among the green stems of the bamboos. But he did not find her. He called, "Yoné! Yoné!" and again, "Yoné! Yoné!" But he had no answer; only the wind sighed in the dry bamboo leaves. Then he felt in his sleeve and brought forth the little flute, and very tenderly put it to his lips. There was a faint sighing sound. Then a voice spoke, thin and pitiful:

"Father, dear father, my wicked stepmother killed me. Three moons since she killed me. She buried me in the clearing of the Bamboo Grove. You may find my bones. As for me, you will never see me any more—you will never see me more...."

—

With his own two-handed sword the man did justice, and slew his wicked wife, avenging the death of his innocent child. Then he dressed himself in coarse white raiment, with a great rice-straw hat that shadowed his face. And he took a staff and a straw rain-coat and bound sandals on his feet, and thus he set forth upon a pilgrimage to the holy places of Japan.

And he carried the little flute with him, in a fold of his garment, upon his breast.

THE TEA-KETTLE

Long ago, as I've heard tell, there dwelt at the temple of Morinji, in the Province of Kotsuke, a holy priest.

Now there were three things about this reverend man. First, he was wrapped up in meditations and observances and forms and doctrines. He was a great one for the Sacred Sutras, and knew strange and mystical things. Then he had a fine exquisite taste of his own, and nothing pleased him so much as the ancient tea ceremony of the *Cha-no-yu*; and for the third thing about him, he knew both sides of a copper coin well enough and loved a bargain.

None so pleased as he when he happened upon an ancient tea-kettle, lying rusty and dirty and half-forgotten in a corner of a poor shop in a back street of his town.

"An ugly bit of old metal," says the holy man to the shop-keeper; "but it will do well enough to boil my humble drop of water of an evening. I'll give you three *rin* for it." This he did and took the kettle home, rejoicing; for it was of bronze, fine work, the very thing for the *Cha-no-yu*.

A novice cleaned and scoured the tea-kettle, and it came out as pretty as you please. The priest turned it this way and that, and upside down, looked into it, tapped it with his finger-nail. He smiled. "A bargain," he cried, "a bargain!" and rubbed his hands. He set the kettle upon a box covered over with a purple cloth, and looked at it so long that first he was fain to rub his eyes many times, and then to close them altogether. His head dropped forward and he slept.

And then, believe me, the wonderful thing happened. The tea-kettle moved, though no hand was near it. A hairy head, with two bright eyes, looked out of the spout. The lid jumped up and down. Four brown and hairy paws appeared, and a fine bushy tail. In a minute the kettle was down from the box and going round and round looking at things.

"A very comfortable room, to be sure," says the tea-kettle.

Pleased enough to find itself so well lodged, it soon began to dance and to caper nimbly and to sing at the top of its voice. Three or four novices were studying in the next room. "The old man is lively," they said; "only hark to him. What can he be at?" And they laughed in their sleeves.

Heaven's mercy, the noise that the tea-kettle made! Bang! bang! Thud! thud! thud!

The novices soon stopped laughing. One of them slid aside the *kara-kami* and peeped through.

"Arah, the devil and all's in it!" he cried. "Here's the master's old tea-kettle turned into a sort of a badger. The gods protect us from witchcraft, or for certain we shall be lost!"

"And I scoured it not an hour since," said another novice, and he fell to reciting the Holy Sutras on his knees.

A third laughed. "I'm for a nearer view of the hobgoblin," he said.

So the lot of them left their books in a twinkling, and gave chase to the tea-kettle to catch it. But could they come up with the tea-kettle? Not a bit of it. It danced and it leapt and it flew up into the air. The novices rushed here and there, slipping upon the mats. They grew hot. They grew breathless.

"Ha, ha! Ha, ha!" laughed the tea-kettle; and "Catch me if you can!" laughed the wonderful tea-kettle.

Presently the priest awoke, all rosy, the holy man.

"And what's the meaning of this racket," he says, "disturbing me at my holy meditations and all?"

"Master, master," cry the novices, panting and mopping their brows, "your tea-kettle is bewitched. It was a badger, no less. And the dance it has been giving us, you'd never believe!"

"Stuff and nonsense," says the priest; "bewitched? Not a bit of it. There it rests on its box, good quiet thing, just where I put it."

Sure enough, so it did, looking as hard and cold and innocent as you please. There was not a hair of a badger near it. It was the novices that looked foolish.

"A likely story indeed," says the priest. "I have heard of the pestle that took wings to itself and flew away, parting company with the mortar. That is easily to be understood by any man. But a kettle that turned into a badger—no, no! To your books, my sons, and pray to be preserved from the perils of illusion."

That very night the holy man filled the kettle with water from the spring and set it on the *hibachi* to boil for his cup of tea. When the water began to boil—

"Ai! Ai!" the kettle cried; "Ai! Ai! The heat of the Great Hell!" And it lost no time at all, but hopped off the fire as quick as you please.

"Sorcery!" cried the priest. "Black magic! A devil! A devil! A devil! Mercy on me! Help! Help! Help!" He was frightened out of his wits, the dear good man. All the novices came running to see what was the matter.

"The tea-kettle is bewitched," he gasped; "it was a badger, assuredly it was a badger ... it both speaks and leaps about the room."

"Nay, master," said a novice, "see where it rests upon its box, good quiet thing."

And sure enough, so it did.

"Most reverend sir," said the novice, "let us all pray to be preserved from the perils of illusion."

The priest sold the tea-kettle to a tinker and got for it twenty copper coins.

"It's a mighty fine bit of bronze," says the priest. "Mind, I'm giving it away to you, I'm sure I cannot tell what for." Ah, he was the one for a bargain! The tinker was a happy man and carried home the kettle. He turned it this way and that, and upside down, and looked into it.

"A pretty piece," says the tinker; "a very good bargain." And when he went to bed that night he put the kettle by him, to see it first thing in the morning.

He awoke at midnight and fell to looking at the kettle by the bright light of the moon.

Presently it moved, though there was no hand near it.

"Strange," said the tinker; but he was a man who took things as they came.

A hairy head, with two bright eyes, looked out of the kettle's spout. The lid jumped up and down. Four brown and hairy paws appeared, and a fine bushy tail. It came quite close to the tinker and laid a paw upon him.

"Well?" says the tinker.

"I am not wicked," says the tea-kettle.

"No," says the tinker.

"But I like to be well treated. I am a badger tea-kettle."

"So it seems," says the tinker.

"At the temple they called me names, and beat me and set me on the fire. I couldn't stand it, you know."

"I like your spirit," says the tinker.

"I think I shall settle down with you."

"Shall I keep you in a lacquer box?" says the tinker.

"Not a bit of it, keep me with you; let us have a talk now and again. I am very fond of a pipe. I like rice to eat, and beans and sweet things."

"A cup of *saké* sometimes?" says the tinker.

"Well, yes, now you mention it."

"I'm willing," says the tinker.

"Thank you kindly," says the tea-kettle; "and, as a beginning, would you object to my sharing your bed? The night has turned a little chilly."

"Not the least in the world," says the tinker.

The tinker and the tea-kettle became the best of friends. They ate and talked together. The kettle knew a thing or two and was very good company.

One day: "Are you poor?" says the kettle.

"Yes," says the tinker, "middling poor."

"Well, I have a happy thought. For a tea-kettle, I am out-of-the-way—really very accomplished."

"I believe you," says the tinker.

"My name is *Bumbuku-Chagama*; I am the very prince of Badger Tea-Kettles."

"Your servant, my lord," says the tinker.

"If you'll take my advice," says the tea-kettle, "you'll carry me round as a show; I really am out-of-the-way, and it's my opinion you'd make a mint of money."

"That would be hard work for you, my dear *Bumbuku*," says the tinker.

"Not at all; let us start forthwith," says the tea-kettle.

So they did. The tinker bought hangings for a theatre, and he called the show *Bumbuku-Chagama*. How the people flocked to see the fun! For the wonderful and most accomplished tea-kettle danced and sang, and walked the tight rope as to the manner born. It played such tricks and had such droll ways that the people laughed till their sides ached. It was a treat to see the tea-kettle bow as gracefully as a lord and thank the people for their patience.

The *Bumbuku-Chagama* was the talk of the country-side, and all the gentry came to see it as well as the commonalty. As for the tinker, he waved a fan and took the money. You may believe that he grew fat and rich. He even went to Court, where the great ladies and the royal princesses made much of the wonderful tea-kettle.

At last the tinker retired from business, and to him the tea-kettle came with tears in its bright eyes.

"I'm much afraid it's time to leave you," it says.

"Now, don't say that, *Bumbuku*, dear," says the tinker. "We'll be so happy together now we are rich."

"I've come to the end of my time," says the tea-kettle. "You'll not see old *Bumbuku* any more; henceforth I shall be an ordinary kettle, nothing more or less."

"Oh, my dear *Bumbuku*, what shall I do?" cried the poor tinker in tears.

"I think I should like to be given to the temple of Morinji, as a very sacred treasure," says the tea-kettle.

It never spoke or moved again. So the tinker presented it as a very sacred treasure to the temple, and the half of his wealth with it.

And the tea-kettle was held in wondrous fame for many a long year. Some persons even worshipped it as a saint.

THE PEONY LANTERN

In Yedo there dwelt a *samurai* called Hagiwara. He was a *samurai* of the *hatamoto*, which is of all the ranks of *samurai* the most honourable. He possessed a noble figure and a very beautiful face, and was beloved of many a lady of Yedo, both openly and in secret. For himself, being yet very young, his thoughts turned to pleasure rather than to love, and morning, noon and night he was wont to disport himself with the gay youth of the city. He was the prince and leader of joyous revels within doors and without, and would often parade the streets for long together with bands of his boon companions.

One bright and wintry day during the Festival of the New Year he found himself with a company of laughing youths and maidens playing at battledore and shuttlecock. He had wandered far away from his own quarter of the city, and was now in a suburb quite the other side of Yedo, where the streets were empty, more or less, and the quiet houses stood in gardens. Hagiwara wielded his heavy battledore with great skill and grace, catching the gilded shuttlecock and tossing it lightly into the air; but at length with a careless or an ill-judged stroke, he sent it flying over the heads of the players, and over the bamboo fence of a garden near by. Immediately he started after it. Then his companions cried, "Stay, Hagiwara; here we have more than a dozen shuttlecocks."

"Nay," he said, "but this was dove-coloured and gilded."

"Foolish one!" answered his friends; "here we have six shuttlecocks all dove-coloured and gilded."

But he paid them no heed, for he had become full of a very strange desire for the shuttlecock he had lost. He scaled the bamboo fence and dropped into the garden which was upon the farther side. Now he had marked the very spot where the shuttlecock should have fallen, but it was not there; so he searched along the foot of the bamboo fence—but no, he could not find it. Up and down he went, beating the bushes with his battledore, his eyes on the ground, drawing breath heavily as if he had lost his dearest treasure. His friends called him, but he did not come, and they grew tired and went to their own homes. The light of day began to fail. Hagiwara, the *samurai*, looked up and saw a girl standing a few yards away from him. She beckoned him with her right hand, and in her left she held a gilded shuttlecock with dove-coloured feathers.

The *samurai* shouted joyfully and ran forward. Then the girl drew away from him, still beckoning him with the right hand. The shuttlecock lured him, and he followed. So they went, the two of them, till they came to the house that was in the garden, and three stone steps that led up to it. Beside the lowest step there grew a plum tree in blossom, and upon the highest step there stood a fair and very young lady. She was most splendidly attired in robes of high festival. Her *kimono* was of water-blue silk, with sleeves of ceremony so long that they touched the ground; her under-dress was scarlet, and her great girdle of brocade was stiff and heavy with gold. In her hair were pins of gold and tortoiseshell and coral.

When Hagiwara saw the lady, he knelt down forthwith and made her due obeisance, till his forehead touched the ground.

Then the lady spoke, smiling with pleasure like a child. "Come into my house, Hagiwara Sama, *samurai* of the *hatamoto*. I am O'Tsuyu, the Lady of the Morning Dew. My dear handmaiden, O'Yoné, has brought you to me. Come in, Hagiwara Sama, *samurai* of the *hatamoto*; for indeed I am glad to see you, and happy is this hour."

So the *samurai* went in, and they brought him to a room of ten mats, where they entertained him; for the Lady of the Morning Dew danced before him in the ancient manner, whilst O'Yoné, the handmaiden, beat upon a small scarlet-tasselled drum.

Afterwards they set food before him, the red rice of the festival and sweet warm wine, and he ate and drank of the food they gave him.

It was dark night when Hagiwara took his leave. "Come again, honourable lord, come again," said O'Yoné the handmaiden.

"Yea, lord, you needs must come," whispered the Lady of the Morning Dew.

The *samurai* laughed. "And if I do not come?" he said mockingly. "What if I do not come?"

The lady stiffened, and her child's face grew grey, but she laid her hand upon Hagiwara's shoulder.

"Then," she said, "it will be death, lord. Death it will be for you and for me. There is no other way." O'Yoné shuddered and hid her eyes with her sleeve.

The *samurai* went out into the night, being very much afraid.

Long, long he sought for his home and could not find it, wandering in the black darkness from end to end of the sleeping city. When at last he reached his familiar door the late dawn was almost come, and wearily he threw himself upon his bed. Then he laughed. "After all, I have left behind me my shuttlecock," said Hagiwara the *samurai*.

The next day Hagiwara sat alone in his house from morning till evening. He had his hands before him; and he thought, but did nothing more. At the end of the time he said, "It is a joke that a couple of *geisha* have sought to play on me. Excellent, in faith, but they shall not have me!" So he dressed himself in his best and went forth to join his friends. For five or six days he was at joustings and junketings, the gayest of the gay. His wit was ready, his spirits were wild.

Then he said, "By the gods, I am deathly sick of this," and took to walking the streets of Yedo alone. From end to end of the great city he went. He wandered by day and he wandered by night, by street and alley he went, by hill and moat and castle wall, but he found not what he sought. He could not come upon the garden where his shuttlecock was lost, nor yet upon the Lady of the Morning Dew. His spirit had no rest. He fell sick and took to his bed, where he neither ate nor slept, but grew spectre-thin. This was about the third month. In the sixth month, at the time of *niubai*, the hot and rainy season, he rose up, and, in spite of all his faithful servant could say or do to dissuade him, he wrapped a loose summer robe about him and at once went forth.

"Alack! Alack!" cried the servant, "the youth has the fever, or he is perchance mad."

Hagiwara faltered not at all. He looked neither to the right nor to the left. Straight forward he went, for he said to himself, "All roads lead past my love's house." Soon he came to a quiet suburb, and to a certain house whose garden had a split bamboo fence. Hagiwara laughed softly and scaled the fence.

"The same, the very same shall be the manner of our meeting," he said. He found the garden wild and overgrown. Moss covered the three stone steps. The plum tree that grew there fluttered its green leaves disconsolate. The house was still, its shutters were all closed, it was forlorn and deserted.

The *samurai* grew cold as he stood and wondered. A soaking rain fell.

There came an old man into the garden. He said to Hagiwara:

"Sir, what do you do here?"

"The white flower has fallen from the plum tree," said the *samurai*. "Where is the Lady of the Morning Dew?"

"She is dead," answered the old man; "dead these five or six moons, of a strange and sudden sickness. She lies in the graveyard on the hill, and O'Yoné, her handmaid, lies by her side. She could not suffer her mistress to wander alone through the long night of Yomi. For their sweet spirits' sake I would still tend this garden, but I am old and it is little that I can do. Oh, sir, they are dead indeed. The grass grows on their graves."

Hagiwara went to his own home. He took a slip of pure white wood and he wrote upon it, in large fair characters, the dear name of his lady. This he set up, and burned before it incense and sweet odours, and made every offering that was meet, and did due observance, and all for the welfare of her departed spirit.

Then drew near the Festival of *Bon*, the time of returning souls. The good folk of Yedo took lanterns and visited their graves. Bringing food and flowers, they cared for their beloved dead. On the thirteenth day of the seventh month, which, in the *Bon*, is the day of days, Hagiwara the *samurai* walked in his garden by night for the sake of the coolness. It was windless and dark. A cicala hidden in the heart of a pomegranate flower sang shrilly now and again. Now and again a carp leaped in the round pond. For the rest it was still, and never a leaf stirred.

About the hour of the Ox, Hagiwara heard the sound of footsteps in the lane that lay beyond his garden hedge. Nearer and nearer they came.

"Women's *geta*," said the *samurai*. He knew them by the hollow echoing noise. Looking over his rose hedge, he saw two slender women come out of the dimness hand in hand. One of them carried a lantern with a bunch of peony flowers tied to the handle. It was such a lantern as is used at the time of the *Bon* in the service of the dead. It swung as the two women walked, casting an uncertain light. As they came abreast of the *samurai* upon the other side of the hedge, they turned their faces to him. He knew them at once, and gave one great cry.

The girl with the peony lantern held it up so that the light fell upon him.

"Hagiwara Sama," she cried, "by all that is most wonderful! Why, lord, we were told that you were dead. We have daily recited the *Nembutsu* for your soul these many moons!"

"Come in, come in, O'Yoné," he said; "and is it indeed your mistress that you hold by the hand? Can it be my lady?... Oh, my love!"

O'Yoné answered, "Who else should it be?" and the two came in at the garden gate.

But the Lady of the Morning Dew held up her sleeve to hide her face.

"How was it I lost you?" said the *samurai*; "how was it I lost you, O'Yoné?"

"Lord," she said, "we have moved to a little house, a very little house, in the quarter of the city which is called the Green Hill. We were suffered to take nothing with us there, and we are grown very poor. With grief and want my mistress is become pale."

Then Hagiwara took his lady's sleeve to draw it gently from her face.

"Lord," she sobbed, "you will not love me, I am not fair."

But when he looked upon her his love flamed up within him like a consuming fire, and shook him from head to foot. He said never a word.

She drooped. "Lord," she murmured, "shall I go or stay?"

And he said, "Stay."

A little before daybreak the *samurai* fell into a deep sleep, and awoke to find himself alone in the clear light of the morning. He lost not an instant, but rose and went forth, and immediately made his way through Yedo to the quarter of the city which is called the Green Hill. Here he inquired for the house of the Lady of the Morning Dew, but no one could direct him. High and low he searched fruitlessly. It seemed to him that for the second time he had lost his dear lady, and he turned homewards in bitter despair. His way led him through the grounds of a certain temple, and as he went he marked two graves that were side by side. One was little and obscure, but the other was marked by a fair monument, like the tomb of some great one. Before the monument there hung a lantern with a bunch of peony flowers tied to its handle. It was such a lantern as is used at the time of *Bon* in the service of the dead.

Long, long did the *samurai* stand as one in a dream. Then he smiled a little and said:

"'*We have moved to a little house ... a very little house ... upon the Green Hill ... we were suffered to take nothing with us there and we are grown very poor ... with grief and want my mistress is become pale....*' A little house, a dark house, yet you will make room for me, oh, my beloved, pale one of my desires. We have loved for the space of ten existences, leave me not now ... my dear." Then he went home.

His faithful servant met him and cried:

"Now what ails you, master?"

He said, "Why, nothing at all.... I was never merrier."

But the servant departed weeping, and saying, "The mark of death is on his face ... and I, whither shall I go that bore him as a child in these arms?"

Every night, for seven nights, the maidens with the peony lantern came to Hagiwara's dwelling. Fair weather or foul was the same to them. They came at the hour of the Ox. There was mystic wooing. By the strong bond of illusion the living and the dead were bound together.

On the seventh night the servant of the *samurai*, wakeful with fear and sorrow, made bold to peer into his lord's room through a crack in the wooden shutters. His hair stood on end and his blood ran cold to see Hagiwara in the arms of a fearful thing, smiling up at the horror that was its face, stroking its dank green robe with languid fingers. With daylight the servant made his way to a holy man of his acquaintance. When he had told his tale he asked, "Is there any hope for Hagiwara Sama?"

"Alack," said the holy man, "who can withstand the power of Karma? Nevertheless, there is a little hope." So he told the servant what he must do. Before nightfall, this one had set a sacred text above every door and window-place of his master's house, and he had rolled in the silk of his master's girdle a golden emblem of the Tathagata. When these things were done, Hagiwara being drawn two ways became himself as weak as water. And his servant took him in his arms, laid him upon his bed and covered him lightly, and saw him fall into a deep sleep.

At the hour of the Ox there was heard the sound of footsteps in the lane, without the garden hedge. Nearer and nearer they came. They grew slow and stopped.

"What means this, O'Yoné, O'Yoné?" said a piteous voice. "The house is asleep, and I do not see my lord."

"Come home, sweet lady, Hagiwara's heart is changed."

"That I will not, O'Yoné, O'Yoné ... you must find a way to bring me to my lord."

"Lady, we cannot enter here. See the Holy Writing over every door and window-place ... we may not enter here."

There was a sound of bitter weeping and a long wail.

"Lord, I have loved thee through the space of ten existences." Then the footsteps retreated and their echo died away.

The next night it was quite the same. Hagiwara slept in his weakness; his servant watched; the wraiths came and departed in sobbing despair.

The third day, when Hagiwara went to the bath, a thief stole the emblem, the golden emblem of the Tathagata, from his girdle. Hagiwara did not mark it. But that night he lay awake. It was his servant that slept, worn out with watching. Presently a great rain fell and Hagiwara, waking, heard the sound of it upon the roof. The heavens were opened and for hours the rain fell. And it tore the holy text from over the round window in Hagiwara's chamber.

At the hour of the Ox there was heard the sound of footsteps in the lane without the garden hedge. Nearer and nearer they came. They grew slow and stopped.

"This is the last time, O'Yoné, O'Yoné, therefore bring me to my lord. Think of the love of ten existences. Great is the power of Karma. There must be a way...."

"Come, my beloved," called Hagiwara with a great voice.

"Open, lord ... open and I come."

But Hagiwara could not move from his couch.

"Come, my beloved," he called for the second time.

"I cannot come, though the separation wounds me like a sharp sword. Thus we suffer for the sins of a former life." So the lady spoke and moaned like the lost soul that she was. But O'Yoné took her hand.

"See the round window," she said.

Hand in hand the two rose lightly from the earth. Like vapour they passed through the unguarded window. The *samurai* called, "Come to me, beloved," for the third time.

He was answered, "Lord, I come."

In the grey morning Hagiwara's servant found his master cold and dead. At his feet stood the peony lantern burning with a weird yellow flame. The servant shivered, took up the lantern and blew out the light; for "I cannot bear it," he said.

THE SEA KING AND THE MAGIC JEWELS

This is a tale beloved by the children of Japan, and by the old folk—a tale of magical jewels and a visit to the Sea King's palace.

Prince Rice-Ear-Ruddy-Plenty loved a beautiful and royal maiden, and made her his bride. And the lady was called Princess Blossoming- Brightly-as-the-Flowers-of-the-Trees, so sweetly fair was she. But her father was augustly wrath at her betrothal, for his Augustness, Prince Rice-Ear-Ruddy-Plenty, had put aside her elder sister, the Princess of the Rocks (and, indeed, this lady was not fair), for he loved only Princess Blossoming-Brightly. So the old King said, "Because of this, the offspring of these heavenly deities shall be frail, fading and falling like the flowers of the trees." So it is. At this day, the lives of their Augustnesses, the Heavenly Sovereigns, are not long.

Howbeit, in the fullness of time, the lady, Blossoming-Brightly-as-the-Flowers-of-the-Trees, bore two lovely men children, and called the elder Fire Flash and the younger Fire Fade.

Prince Fire Flash was a fisherman, who got his luck upon the wide sea, and ran upon the shore with his august garments girded. And again, he tarried all the night in his boat, upon the high wave-crests. And he caught things broad of fin and things narrow of fin, and he was a deity of the water weeds and of the waters and of the fishes of the sea.

But Prince Fire Fade was a hunter, who got his luck upon the mountains and in the forest, who bound sandals fast upon his feet, and bore a bow and heavenly-feathered arrows. And he caught things rough of hair and things soft of hair, and he knew the trail of the badger and the wild cherry's time of flowering. For he was a deity of the woods.

Now Prince Fire Fade spoke to his elder brother, Prince Fire Flash, and said, "Brother, I am aweary of the green hills. Therefore let us now exchange our luck. Give me thy rod and I will go to the cool waters. Thou mayest take my great bow and all my heavenly-feathered arrows and try the mountains, where, trust me, thou shalt see many strange and beautiful things, unknown to thee before."

But Prince Fire Flash answered, "Not so ... not so."

And again, after not many days were past, Prince Fire Fade came and sighed, "I am aweary of the green hills ... the fair waters call me. Woe to be a younger brother!" And when Prince Fire Flash took no heed of him, but angled with his rod, day and night, and caught things broad of fin and things narrow of fin, Prince Fire Fade drooped with desire, and let his long hair fall untended upon his shoulders. And he murmured, "Oh, to try my luck upon the sea!" till at last Prince Fire Flash, his elder brother, gave him the rod for very weariness, and betook himself to the mountains. And all day he hunted, and let fly the heavenly-feathered arrows; but rough of hair or soft of hair, never a thing did he catch. And he cried, "Fool, fool, to barter the heavenly luck of the gods!" So he returned.

And his Augustness, Prince Fire Fade, took the luck of the sea, and angled in sunshine and in gloom; but broad of fin or narrow of fin, never a fish did he catch. And, moreover, he lost his brother's fish-hook in the sea. So he hung his head, and returned.

And Prince Fire Flash said, "Each to his own, the hunter

to the mountain, and the fisherman to the sea ... for thou and I have brought nothing home, and this night we sleep hungry. We may not barter the luck of the gods. And now, where is my fish-hook?"

So Prince Fire Fade replied, saying softly, "Sweet brother, be not angry ... but, toiling all day with thy fish-hook, broad of fin or narrow of fin, not a fish did I catch; and, at the last, I lost thy fish-hook in the sea."

At this his Highness, Prince Fire Flash, flew into a great rage, and stamping his feet, required the fish-hook of his brother.

And Prince Fire Fade made answer, "Sweet brother, I have not thy fish-hook, but the deep sea, whose bottom no man may search. Though I should die for thee, yet could I not give thee back thy fish-hook."

But his elder brother required it of him the more urgently.

Then Prince Fire Fade burst the wild wistaria tendrils which bound his august ten-grasp sword to his side. And he said, "Farewell, good sword." And he broke it into many fragments, and made five hundred fish-hooks to give to his brother, Prince Fire Flash. But Prince Fire Flash would have none of them.

And again Prince Fire Fade toiled at a great furnace, and made one thousand fish-hooks; and upon his knees he humbly offered them to his brother, Prince Fire Flash. For he loved his brother. Nevertheless Prince Fire Flash would not so much as look at them, but sat moody, his head on his hand, saying, "Mine own lost fish-hook will I have, that and no other."

So Prince Fire Fade went grieving from the palace gates, and wandered lamenting by the seashore; and his tears fell and mingled with the foam. And, when night came, he had no heart to return homewards, but sat down, weary, upon a rock amid the salt pools. And he cried, "Alas, my brother, I am all to blame, and through my foolishness has this come upon me. But oh, my brother, together were we nursed upon the sweet breast of our mother, Princess Blossoming-Brightly-as-the-Flowers-of-the-Trees, for almost hand in hand did we come into the world."

And the moon rose so that the sea and the Central Land of Reed Plains was light. But Prince Fire Fade ceased not to lament.

Then Shiko-Tsuchi-no-Kami, the Lord of Sea Salt, came with the rising tide, and spoke, "Wherefore weeps the Heaven's Sky Height?"

And Prince Fire Fade made answer: "I have taken my brother's fish-hook, and I have lost it in the sea. And though I have given him many other fish-hooks for compensation, he will have none of them, but desires only the original fish-hook. Truly, the gods know, I would give my life to find it; but how should that serve?"

And Shiko-Tsuchi-no-Kami took him by the sleeve to where a boat moved upon the water, and set him in the boat and pushed it from the shore, saying, "My son, pursue the pleasant path that Tsuki-Yomi-no-Kami, His Augustness, the Moon Night Possessor, has made for thee upon the waters. And, at the end, thou shalt come to a palace made of fishes' scales, which is the palace of the great King of the Sea. Before the gate there is a clear well, and by the well-side there grows a cassia tree with many spreading branches. Therefore climb thou into the branches of the cassia tree, and there wait for the King's daughter, who shall come to give thee counsel."

And Prince Fire Fade, standing up in the boat, made obeisance, and thanked the Lord of Sea Salt. But this one girded his august garments and pushed the boat before him, till he was thigh-deep in the water. And he said, "Nay, nay, fair youth, no thanks, only do my bidding."

So his Augustness, Prince Fire Fade, came to the Sea King's palace. And he forthwith climbed the cassia tree and waited among its green branches.

At the day's dawning came the handmaidens of the Sea King's daughter, with their jewelled vessels, to draw water from the well. And as they stooped to dip their vessels, Prince Fire Fade leaned and watched them from the branches of the cassia tree. And the glory of his august countenance made a brightness upon the waters of the well. So all the maidens looked up and beheld his comeliness, and were amazed. But he spoke them fairly, and desired of them a little water from their vessels. So the maidens drew him water in a jewelled cup (howbeit the jewels were clouded, because of the coldness of the well water), and they presented it to him with all reverence. Then, not drinking the water, Prince Fire Fade took the royal jewel from his neck, and holding it between his two lips he dropped it into the cup, and the cup he gave again to the maidens.

Now they saw the great jewel shining in the cup, but they could not move it, for it clung fast to the gold. So the maidens departed, skimming the water like the white birds of the offing. And they came to the Sea King's daughter, bearing the cup and the jewel in it.

And the Princess, looking at the jewel, asked them, "Is there, perchance, a stranger at the gate?"

And one of the maidens answered, "There is some one

sitting in the branches of the cassia tree which is by our well."

And another said, "It is a very beautiful young man."

And another said, "He is even more glorious than our king. And he asked water of us, so we respectfully gave him water in this cup. And he drank none of it, but dropped a jewel into it from his lips. So we have brought them unto Thine Augustness, both the cup and the jewel."

Then the Princess herself took a vessel and went to draw water at the well. And her long sleeves, and certain of the folds of her august garments, floated behind her, and her head was bound with a garland of sea flowers. And coming to the well she looked up through the branches of the cassia tree. And her eyes met the eyes of Prince Fire Fade.

And presently she fetched her father, the Sea King, saying, "Father, there is a beautiful person at our gate." So the Sea King came out and welcomed Prince Fire Fade, and said, "This is the August Child of the Heaven's Sun Height." And leading him into his palace he caused the floor to be spread with eight layers of rugs of asses' skins, and eight layers of rugs of silk, and set the Prince upon them.

And that night he made a great banquet, and celebrated the betrothal of Prince Fire Fade to his daughter, the fair Jewel Princess. And for very many days there was held high revel and rejoicing in the Sea King's palace.

But one night, as they took their ease upon the silken floor, and all the fishes of the sea brought rich dishes, and sweetmeats in vessels of gold and coral and jade to set before them, the fair Jewel Princess herself sat at Prince Fire Fade's right hand to pour the wine into his cup. And the silver scales upon the palace walls glittered in the moonlight. But Prince Fire Fade looked out across the Sea Path and thought of what had gone before, and so heaved a deep sigh.

Then the Sea King was troubled, and asked him, saying, "Wherefore dost thou sigh?" But Prince Fire Fade answered nothing.

And the fair Jewel Princess, his betrothed wife, came closer, and touched him on the breast, and said softly, "Oh, Thine Augustness, my sweet spouse, art thou not happy in our water palace, where the shadows fall green, that thou lookest so longingly across the Sea Path? Or do our maidens not please thee, who move silently, like the birds of the offing? Oh, my lord, despise me not, but tell me what is in thine heart."

Then Prince Fire Fade answered, "My lovely lady, Thine Augustness, let nothing be hidden from thee, because of our love." And he told them all the story of the fish-hook, and of his elder brother's wrath.

"And now," he said, "will the Jewel Princess give me counsel?"

Then the Jewel Princess smiled, and rose up lightly, and her hair was so long that it hung to the edge and hem of her silken red robe. And she passed to where the palace steps led down into the water. And standing upon the last step she called to the fishes of the sea, and summoned them, great and small, from far and near. So the fishes of the sea, both great and small, swam about her feet, and the water was silver with their scales. And the King's daughter cried, "O fishes of the sea, find and bring me the august fish-hook of Prince Fire Flash."

And the fishes answered, "Lady, the *Tai* is in misery, for something sticks in his throat so that he cannot eat. Perchance this may be the august fish-hook of his Augustness, Prince Fire Flash."

Then the Princess stooped down and lifted the *Tai* from the water, and with her white hand she took the lost fish-hook from his throat. And after she had washed and dabbled it for a little, she took it in to Prince Fire Fade. And he rejoiced and said, "This is indeed my brother's fish-hook. I go to restore it instantly, and we shall be reconciled." For he loved his brother.

But the fair Jewel Princess stood silent and sorrowing, for she thought, "Now will he depart and leave me lonely."

And Prince Fire Fade hastened to the water's edge, and there bestrode a valiant crocodile, who should bring him to his journey's end. And ere he went, the Sea King spoke: "Fair youth, now listen to my counsel. If thy brother sow rice upon the uplands, do thou sow thy rice low, in the water meads. But if thy brother sow his rice in the water meads, then do thou, Thine Augustness, sow thy rice upon the uplands. And I who rule the rains and the floods will continually prosper the labours of Thine Augustness. Moreover, here are two magic jewels. If thy brother should be moved by envy to attack thee, then put forth the Tide Flowing Jewel and the waters shall arise to drown him. But if thou shouldst have compassion upon him, then put forth the Tide Ebbing Jewel, and all the waters shall subside, and his life be spared."

And his Augustness Prince Fire Fade gave thanks with obeisance. And he hid the fish-hook in his long sleeve, and hung the two great jewels about his neck. Then the fair Jewel Princess came near and bade him farewell, with many tears. And the Sea King charged the crocodile, saying, "While crossing the middle of the sea, do not alarm him."

So Prince Fire Fade sat upon the crocodile's head; and in one day he came to his own place and sprang lightly to shore.

And unsheathing his dagger, he hung it upon the crocodile's neck for a token.

Hereupon, Prince Fire Fade found his brother, and gave him back his own fish-hook that had been lost. Nevertheless, because of the two great jewels, which he wore in the folds of his raiment, he had everlasting dominion over his brother, and flourished in all his doings.

And, after some time, there came to Prince Fire Fade the daughter of the Sea King, the fair Jewel Princess. And she came across the Sea Path bearing in her arms a young child. And she, weeping, laid down the child at the feet of His Augustness and said, "My lord, I have brought thy son."

But Prince Fire Fade raised her up and made her welcome, and built for her a palace on the seashore, at the limit of the waves. And the palace was thatched with cormorant's feathers. So they dwelt there with the August Child.

And the fair Jewel Princess besought her lord, saying, "Sweet husband, look not on me in the dark night, for then I must take my native shape; with those of my land it is ever so. Howbeit, look not on me, lest I should be ashamed and misfortune should follow." So Prince Fire Fade promised her, and spoke many fair words of assurance.

Nevertheless, there came a night when Prince Fire Fade lay awake, and could get no rest. And, at length, when it was very dark, before the dawn, he arose and struck a light to look upon his bride as she slept. And he beheld a great scalèd dragon, with translucent eyes, which was coiled up at the couch's foot. And Prince Fire Fade cried out aloud for terror, and dropped the light. Then morning broke very grey upon the sea. And at the same instant the great dragon stirred, and from its coils the Jewel Princess lifted up her lovely head.

And the green scales fell away from her like a garment. So she stood, in a white robe, with her child upon her breast. And she hung her head and wept, saying, "O Thine Augustness, my sweet spouse, I had thought to have made the Sea Path a highway between thy land and mine, that we might go and come at pleasure. But now, though I warned thee, thou hast looked upon me in the night. Therefore, my lord, between me and thee it is farewell. I go across the Sea Path, and of this going there is no return. Take thou the August Child."

She spoke, and departed immediately upon the Sea Path, weeping and covering her face with her hair and looking back to the shore. And she was never more seen upon the Central Land of Reed Plains. Moreover, she shut the gates of the sea and closed the way to her father's palace. But the young maid, her sister, she sent to be a nurse to her babe, and because, for all that had been, she could not restrain her loving heart, she made a little song, and sent it to her lord by the maid, her sister. And the song said:

"Oh, fair are the red jewels,

And fair is the string on which they are strung ...

Even so, fair is my babe.

But brighter far, and more renowned are the white jewels,

The jewels that are like my lord."

Then the husband answered, in a song which said:

"As for thee, my lady, whom I took to be my bride, To the island where lights the wild duck—the bird of the offing, I shall not forget thee till the end of my life."

THE GOOD THUNDER

Folks say that Rai-den, the Thunder, is an unloving spirit, fearful and revengeful, cruel to man. These are folks who are mortally afraid of the storm, and who hate lightning and tempest; they speak all the evil they can of Rai-den and of Rai-Taro, his son. But they are wrong.

Rai-den Sama lived in a Castle of Cloud set high in the blue heaven. He was a great and mighty god, a Lord of the Elements. Rai-Taro was his one and only son, a brave boy, and his father loved him.

In the cool of the evening Rai-den and Rai-Taro walked upon the ramparts of the Castle of Cloud, and from the ramparts they viewed the doings of men upon the Land of Reed Plains. North and South and East and West they looked. Often they laughed—oh, very often; sometimes they sighed. Sometimes Rai-Taro leaned far over the castle walls to see the children that went to and fro upon earth.

One night Rai-den Sama said to Rai-Taro, "Child, look well this night upon the doings of men!"

Rai-Taro answered, "Father, I will look well."

From the northern rampart they looked, and saw great lords and men-at-arms going forth to battle. From the southern rampart they looked, and saw priests and acolytes serving in a holy temple where the air was dim with incense, and images of gold and bronze gleamed in the twilight. From the eastern rampart they looked, and saw a lady's bower, where was a fair princess, and a troop of maidens, clad in rose colour, that made music for her. There were children there, too, playing with a little cart of flowers.

"Ah, the pretty children!" said Rai-Taro.

From the western rampart they looked, and saw a peasant toiling in a rice-field. He was weary enough and his back ached. His wife toiled with him by his side. If he was weary, it is easy to believe that she was more weary still. They were very poor and their garments were ragged.

"Have they no children?" said Rai-Taro. Rai-den shook his head.

Presently, "Have you looked well, Rai-Taro?" he said. "Have you looked well this night upon the doings of men?"

"Father," said Rai-Taro, "indeed, I have looked well."

"Then choose, my son, choose, for I send you to take up your habitation upon the earth."

"Must I go among men?" said Rai-Taro.

"My child, you must."

"I will not go with the men-at-arms," said Rai-Taro; "fighting likes me very ill."

"Oho, say you so, my son? Will you go, then, to the fair lady's bower?"

"No," said Rai-Taro, "I am a man. Neither will I have my head shaved to go and live with priests."

"What, then, do you choose the poor peasant? You will have a hard life and scanty fare, Rai-Taro."

Rai-Taro said, "They have no children. Perhaps they will love me."

"Go, go in peace," said Rai-den Sama; "for you have chosen wisely."

"How shall I go, my father?" said Rai-Taro.

"Honourably," said his father, "as it befits a Prince of High Heaven."

Now the poor peasant man toiled in his rice-field, which was at the foot of the mountain Hakusan, in the province of

Ichizen. Day after day and week after week the bright sun shone. The rice-field was dry, and young rice was burnt up.

"Alack and alas!" cried the poor peasant man, "and what shall I do if my rice-crop fails? May the dear gods have mercy on all poor people!"

With that he sat himself down on a stone at the rice-field's edge and fell asleep for very weariness and sorrow.

When he woke the sky was black with clouds. It was but noonday, but it grew as dark as night. The leaves of the trees shuddered together and the birds ceased their singing.

"A storm, a storm!" cried the peasant. "Rai-den Sama goes abroad upon his black horse, beating the great drum of the Thunder. We shall have rain in plenty, thanks be."

Rain in plenty he had, sure enough, for it fell in torrents, with blinding lightning and roaring thunder.

"Oh, Rai-den Sama," said the peasant, "saving your greatness, this is even more than sufficient."

At this the bright lightning flashed anew and fell to the earth in a ball of living fire, and the heavens cracked with a mighty peal of thunder.

"Ai! Ai!" cried the poor peasant man. "Kwannon have mercy on a sinful soul, for now the Thunder Dragon has me indeed." And he lay on the ground and hid his face.

Howbeit the Thunder Dragon spared him. And soon he sat up and rubbed his eyes. The ball of fire was gone, but a babe lay upon the wet earth; a fine fresh boy with the rain upon his cheeks and his hair.

"Oh, Lady, Lady Kwannon," said the poor peasant man, "this is thy sweet mercy." And he took the boy in his arms and carried him to his own home.

As he went the rain still fell, but the sun came out in the

blue sky, and every flower in the cooler air shone and lifted up its grateful head.

The peasant came to his cottage door.

"Wife, wife," he called, "I have brought you something home."

"What may it be?" said his wife.

The man answered, "Rai-Taro, the little eldest son of the Thunder."

Rai-Taro grew up straight and strong, the tallest, gayest boy of all that country-side. He was the delight of his foster-parents, and all the neighbours loved him. When he was ten years old he worked in the rice-fields like a man. He was the wonderful weather prophet.

"My father," he said, "let us do this and that, for we shall have fair weather"; or he said, "My father, let us the rather do this or that, for to-night there will be a storm," and whatever he had said, so, sure enough, it came to pass. And he brought great good fortune to the poor peasant man, and all his works prospered.

When Rai-Taro was eighteen years old all the neighbours were bidden to his birthday feast. There was plenty of good *saké*, and the good folk were merry enough; only Rai-Taro was silent and sad and sorry.

"What ails you, Rai-Taro?" said his foster-mother. "You who are wont to be the gayest of the gay, why are you silent, sad and sorry?"

"It is because I must leave you," Rai-Taro said.

"Nay," said his foster-mother, "never leave us, Rai-Taro, my son. Why would you leave us?"

"Mother, because I must," said Rai-Taro in tears.

"You have been our great good fortune; you have given

us all things. What have I given you? What have I given you, Rai-Taro, my son?"

Rai-Taro answered, "Three things have you taught me—to labour, to suffer, and to love. I am more learned than the Immortals."

Then he went from them. And in the likeness of a white cloud he scaled heaven's blue height till he gained his father's castle. And Rai-den received him. The two of them stood upon the western rampart of the Castle of Cloud and looked down to earth.

The foster-mother stood weeping bitterly, but her husband took her hand.

"My dear," he said, "it will not be for long. We grow old apace."

For the full listing of our titles visit
www.sophenebooks.com

All of our titles are available on amazon.com, amazon.co.uk,
amazon.de, amazon.fr, amazon.es, and amazon.it

SOPHENE

Made in the USA
Monee, IL
17 December 2019